The **DK** *Art School*

AN INTRODUCTION TO
WATERCOLOUR

The DK Art School

AN INTRODUCTION TO
WATERCOLOUR

RAY SMITH

DORLING KINDERSLEY
LONDON • NEW YORK • SYDNEY • MOSCOW
IN ASSOCIATION WITH THE ROYAL ACADEMY OF ARTS
www.dk.com

A DORLING KINDERSLEY BOOK
www.dk.com

Project editor Emma Foa
Art editor Claire Legemah
Assistant editor Joanna Warwick
Design assistant Dawn Terrey
Senior editor Gwen Edmonds
Senior art editor Toni Kay
Managing editor Sean Moore
Managing art editor Tina Vaughan
DTP manager Joanna Figg-Latham
Production controller Helen Creeke
Photography Phil Gatwood
Additional photography by Susanna Price,
Tim Ridley, Steve Gorton, Andy Crawford

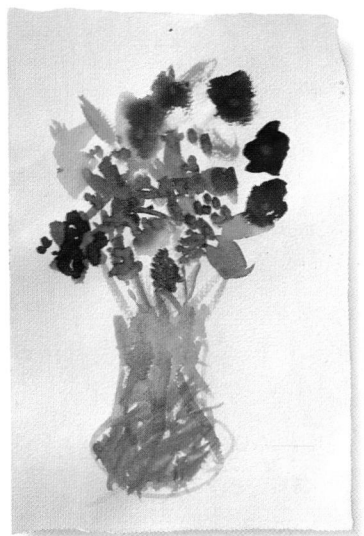

Artists' materials kindly supplied by
Winsor & Newton

This DK Art School /Art book
first published in Great Britain in 1993
by Dorling Kindersley Limited,
80 Strand, London WC2R ORL

Reprinted 1995

ISBN 0 7513 0650 9 PB
First paperback edition 1998

6 8 10 9 7 5

Colour reproduction by Colourscan in Singapore

Printed in China by Toppan Printing Co.,
(Shenzhen) Ltd.

CONTENTS

WATERCOLOUR

OF ALL THE VARIOUS PAINTING MEDIA, including oils and acrylics, watercolour is by far the most convenient to work with. It has the range and adaptability for almost any kind of painting situation or style. All you need to get started is a small watercolour box, a couple of brushes, a pad of paper and some water. When you look at a watercolour painting, you can see how it was painted as well as getting a sense of the artist through the kinds of marks that have been made. This is because the nature of the watercolour painting method is such that almost nothing can be concealed in the painting. Unless you are using gouache paints (*see* pp.64-5), you cannot paint over something in order to conceal it in the way you can when you are painting in either oils or acrylics.

Picking up tips

What this means is that it is possible, just by looking at a painting carefully, to make a reasonably accurate guess at the means by which a particular effect was achieved. The implications of this are that anyone with a little experience and sense of how the medium works should be able to look at the watercolour paintings of artists they admire and to pick up useful practical information. For this reason each section of the book ends with a "gallery" of relevant paintings with examples of both historical and contemporary artists.

The power of transparency

What makes it possible to "read" a painting is that the watercolour medium is above all else a transparent painting medium. It relies for most of its effects on the fact that rays of light penetrate to the watercolour paper and are reflected back to the viewer through the transparent paint film. The more the paint and the darker the washes, the less light is reflected back. In an opaque painting system, the rays of light would be reflected back off the surface of the paint itself rather than the paper, because the paint is too dense for the rays of light to penetrate. There is an opaque watercolour system based on gouache paint or body colour and we shall be considering this later. There are also uses for body colour in largely transparent painting techniques where, for instance, the artist may be working on an off-white or coloured paper and wishes to put in a white highlight. Purist watercolour painters have tended to avoid the use of body colour, favouring overlaid washes of transparent colour and using the white of the paper itself for highlights.

Drawings and colour washes

At its most basic, the watercolour medium provides an effective and "clean" method of applying colour washes to a pencil drawing. For many artists this is the very first stage in the development of their practical knowledge of paint and painting. It is an excellent starting point because, used in this way, watercolour is not at all intimidating and with a little practice the results can look extremely competent. A simple drawing can be transformed by the addition of a couple of washes of colour. It is important for beginners to realize that if they start in this way and follow a few basic guidelines, they can achieve a surprising degree of expertise in a relatively short time.

Getting started

This book is designed to introduce the medium, its tools and techniques in a way that is practical and accessible. The Brief History which follows sets watercolour painting in its historical perspective, while the many "tips" boxes help you to paint successfully. The most essential element in all this is that you enjoy what you are doing. Always paint the things that you want to paint, not the things you imagine you ought to paint. You will no doubt get frustrated at times – all painters do – but keep practising or try another approach until you get it right. Remember also that the quality of your materials is important – you cannot paint a fine line if your brush does not come to a point and thin paper will buckle if it has not been stretched. Having said all that, it is time to look at some fine historical examples of watercolours, and start painting.

Good luck!

A BRIEF HISTORY

THE FLOWERING OF WATERCOLOUR PAINTING in Britain towards the end of the eighteenth century tends to foster the idea that this was when watercolour painting began. In fact, artists had been using water-soluble binding materials with pigments for centuries. As early as the end of the fifteenth century, Albrecht Dürer *(1471-1528)* produced a remarkable series of landscape

paintings which can rightly be called watercolours. Dürer used water-soluble paints on parchment or on paper, overlaying transparent colours and using the colour of the paper for the lights.

Albrecht Dürer, *Lake in the Woods,* **1495-97**
The brooding atmosphere of this famous early watercolour landscape gives it a particularly contemporary feel, with the trees on the left appearing blasted by war. The scene is deserted as if there is not a human being left alive.

THE SEVENTEENTH CENTURY saw a number of monochromatic drawings in pen and ink and wash, or simply in brush and wash, by artists such as Nicolas Poussin *(1594-1665)* and Claude Lorrain *(1600-1682)*. These studies may not technically be categorized as watercolours, yet they are very much the forerunners in style and technique of the work of later watercolour painters.

Towards realism

Wenceslaus Hollar *(1607-1677)* was an artist who came to England from Prague in 1636. His panoramic views of English towns and coastlines were an attempt to make faithful representations of places rather than to create the kinds of imaginary classical landscape we associate with artists like Claude Lorrain.

Among other artists working in this way was Francis Place *(1647-1728)* who, in addition to his many panoramic works, produced a fine series of pen and wash drawings from nature which were characterized by a fluent and highly assured use of brush and wash.

The mid to late eighteenth century saw the emergence of a number of painters who chose to concentrate on watercolour as their preferred medium. Paul Sandby *(1725-1809)* was one of the first British artists to recognize and to fully exploit the potential of the medium in works which incorporated both transparent and body colour techniques. His architect brother Thomas *(1723-1798)* was also a fine watercolour painter with some skill in wash techniques.

J.M.W. Turner RA, *Venice: Looking East from the Giudecca, Sunrise,* **1819**
This atmospheric study (left) is evoked with great economy of brushwork and colour. The warm brown of the foreground creates a sense of distance across the lagoon.

Thomas Girtin,
Bamburgh Castle,
Northumberland,
1797-99
*This strong, fully
resolved landscape
is painted on warm
brown cartridge paper.
In order to highlight
certain details, Girtin
has used touches of
white body colour on
the cows and on the
seagulls on the left as
well as on areas of
the rock face.*

John Robert Cozens,
Chamonix and Martigny, c.1776
*The figures dwarfed by the overhanging rock
and the apparent insignificance of the fir trees
convey the immensity of scale in this vast
mountain landscape.*

John Constable RA, *Landscape with
Trees and a Distant Mansion,* **1805**
*This is a very relaxed study with the warm
yellow-browns of the trees and hedges set
against the blues of the distant landscape and
the sky. Constable liked to make direct studies
from nature. The handling here is assured,
with large, generous brushwork.*

Alexander Cozens *(c.1717-1786)*
made a number of simple economical
studies from nature. His son J.R.
Cozens *(1752-1797)* made landscapes
characterized by their intensity and
the power of the atmosphere they
generate *(centre)*. They have a
breadth of scale in which tiny figures
and buildings are dwarfed by huge
mountains or vast city walls.

By contrast, but no less striking
in their effect, are the paintings of
Francis Towne *(1740-1816)*, whose
almost diagrammatic style is
immediately recognizable for its
sense of form, design and order.

For other contemporary artists
such as Thomas Gainsborough
(1727-1788), watercolour was primarily
used to give colour and tone to chalk
drawings. His studies, with their loose,
vigorous brushstrokes, demonstrate a
remarkable spontaneity of approach.

A new status

Towards the end of the
eighteenth century, two
of the great talents of
watercolour painting
emerged, J.M.W. Turner
(1775-1851) (bottom left) and
Thomas Girtin *(1775-1802)
(top right)*. The quality,
breadth and directness of
their work would bring a
new status to the medium.
It allowed watercolour
paintings to be seen as
works of art in their own
right rather than merely
as coloured drawings
or studies for oil paintings.

Thomas Girtin began to stretch
the watercolour medium further
than it had gone before, trying
out different materials. He made
paintings on rough cartridge papers
so as to be able to work on a more
mid-toned ground. He pared down
his palette and found he could create
all the effects that he needed with
just a limited range of colours.

Ahead of his time

It was J.M.W. Turner, however, who got to grips with watercolour painting as no artist had done before. Not content with mere colouring-in exercises, he constantly experimented with ways of moving the paint around, and with new pigments and papers. He used colour very directly, working wet-into-wet, scrubbing off, sponging and scratching out (*see* pp.56-9).

There were many contemporaries of Turner working both in England and in France who made significant contributions to the art of watercolour painting. John Constable *(1776-1837)* made direct studies from the landscape in a vigorous and very immediate style, often using scraping and scratching out techniques to build up a textured effect. John Sell Cotman *(1782-1842)* produced unique paintings of a quite different order. These are carefully designed works in which flat planes of colour and tone build like a jigsaw over the surface.

The landscapes of David Cox *(1783-1859)* are often turbulent or brooding in spirit. The speed of execution is visible in the large, rich brushstrokes dragged across the rough paper.

19th century developments

The mid to late nineteenth century saw work in watercolour by a number of interesting artists in England, including Samuel Palmer *(1805-1881)* *(right)* and Alfred William Hunt *(1830-1896)*. In France, Camille Pissarro *(1830-1903)*, Paul Gauguin *(1848-1903)* and Paul Cezanne *(1839-1906)* were among the artists who used the medium. Cezanne painted over 400 watercolours and experimented with

transparent effects on white paper and denser body colour effects on toned paper.

The diversity of movements and styles in the development of painting in the twentieth century has been reflected in the great variety of approaches to watercolour.

Camille Pissarro, *An Orchard, c.*1890
This delicate, watery study is one in which the colours are softly fused. But for all its delicacy and softness, it has great strength.

John Sell Cotman,
***Dolbadarn Castle, c.*1802**
Bathed in early evening light, this quiet atmospheric work displays Cotman's characteristic sense of order and design.

Samuel Palmer, *The Herdsman, c.*1855
Palmer's exuberant landscape is a celebration of nature with its richly textured foliage and sense of sunlight. Using a variety of techniques,

Palmer has picked out the foreground highlights with white body colour while in other areas he has scratched off the paint to get back to the white surface of the paper.

John Singer Sargent RA, *Santa Maria della Salute, Venice,* **1907-08**
This is a loose and busy study by an artist who made many fluent sketches in watercolour. Here Sargent has juxtaposed elements of both colour and design as the angular masts and spars of the heavily toned boats cut sharply across the pale, rounded domes in the background.

Edward Hopper, *Captain Kelly's House,* **1931**
This painting has Hopper's characteristic honesty. Nothing is concealed and yet it remains hauntingly enigmatic.

Among the many groups of artists who were influential in reshaping attitudes to the medium were members of a Munich group which included Wassily Kandinsky *(1866-1944)*, Franz Marc *(1880-1916)*, August Macke *(1887-1914)* and Paul Klee *(1879-1940)* (*see* p.36). Kandinsky, born in Moscow, was one of the first to develop an abstract visual language, freeing watercolour from an overly pictorial truth and allowing images to float on the paper.

Klee made many experiments with the medium, working with thin, freely applied washes and also with densely pigmented gouache on a variety of surfaces. His works often have a magical, almost childlike quality.

Across the Atlantic artists such as Winslow Homer *(1836-1910)* and John Singer Sargent *(1856-1925) (top right)* were developing a distinct American style. Sargent spent most of his life in Europe, adapting the skills he had learnt as a portrait painter to a broad range of subjects. He echoed some of Homer's themes while becoming increasingly interested in the interplay of light and colour.

Another American to become interested in the effects of light was Edward Hopper *(1882-1967) (left)*. His watercolours can seem disarmingly straightforward but they are highly charged, demanding a response from the viewer.

One of the most impressive watercolour artists of this century was the German Emil Nolde *(1867-1956) (see p.23)*. He would take his paints with him to the theatre, working by feel in the dark. Like Turner a century earlier, he pushed the medium to its limits, constantly experimenting with techniques and materials. His vast body of work was a celebration of colour and of form, and brought a new richness to the medium.

PAINTS

WATERCOLOUR PAINTS ARE MADE by first mixing and then grinding powder pigments with a water-soluble binding material such as gum arabic. The pigments used to make watercolour paints are in general the same as those used in other types of paint, such as oils or acrylics. Gum arabic is a natural sap taken from the African acacia tree and gets its name from the species *Acacia arabica*. The type most commonly used nowadays is Kordofan gum arabic, which comes from the Sudan.

Early watercolour paint box

Rose Madder root

Pigments
Earth substances and animal substances form the basis of many pigments.

Terre Verte

Cochineal insects

THE GUM IS PREPARED in gum kettles as a 30 per cent solution in water and subsequently mixed into a paste with the pigment. The paste is then ground on granite triple roll mills and, for tube colours, put into tubes, or, in the case of pan colours, dried off in large round cakes like cow-pats before being rammed through a die and extruded in strings. These are then cut to the whole or half-pan size before being wrapped.

Certain additional materials can be added to the basic pigment/gum arabic mixture to create a stable product. These include glycerine, which is a syrupy liquid used in very small amounts to aid the adhesion and flexibility of the paint as well as to keep it moist. In the past, honey was often used for

this purpose. A wetting agent, such as oxgall, is used to help disperse the pigment particles. A thickener is often incorporated when the mix with gum arabic alone is too thin and requires more body. Dextrin is often used for this purpose and is occasionally used as a replacement for gum arabic where a particular pigment will not

How paint is made
The crushed pigment and gum arabic mix are left to dry as slabs of colour (below) before being forced through a die and extruded as strips (below right). These are then cut into segments to form pan colours.

French Ultramarine

Viridian

Yellow Oxide

Cadmium Yellow

Crushed pigments
Pigments are the solid separate particles in various colours that form the basis of watercolour paints. They each have certain characteristics, differing in their strengths, in their lightfastness, and in their degree of transparency.

Slabs of dry colour

Lengths of pan colour

flow out to a flat wash with gum arabic or reacts adversely with it. Dextrin is also used as a substitute for gum arabic in cheap watercolours. It is very re-soluble, and this can affect the success of certain techniques, such as overpainting.

Artists' quality

Raw Sienna

Manufacturers also tend to add a preservative to prevent the growth of mould or bacteria. There is a great art to making the best quality watercolour paints as each pigment will require more or less of each of the ingredients in order for a stable and workable colour to be made. With pan colours, the manufacturer has to ensure that the paint does not dry out in the box but equally, that it does not absorb too much moisture and go soggy. The difference between artists' quality watercolour paints and the cheaper ranges is marked. The pigment loading in the artists' ranges is so high that it

is the pigment that controls the behaviour of the paint. The differences between pan and tube watercolours vary from pigment to pigment, but the main overall difference is that there is more glycerine in the tube colours and this makes them a little more soluble than the pans.

The soft or moist watercolours used today are somewhat different to the early prototypes. J.M.W. Turner, for example, would have used blocks of straight pigment and gum mixes with no added moisturiser – what are now known as "hard" watercolours. Once Turner's washes had dried

Tube and pan colours
Tube colours contain slightly more glycerine than the pans, but not noticeably so. For large washes of colour, tubes are the better option.

Gouache
Gouache or bodycolour is a watercolour paint which is characterized by its opacity.

completely, they would have been easy to overpaint without disturbing the colour underneath (subject to certain differences in particular pigments). Nowadays, if a colour already on the painting is at fairly full strength, for example, it can be difficult to overpaint it without re-dissolving it to some extent.

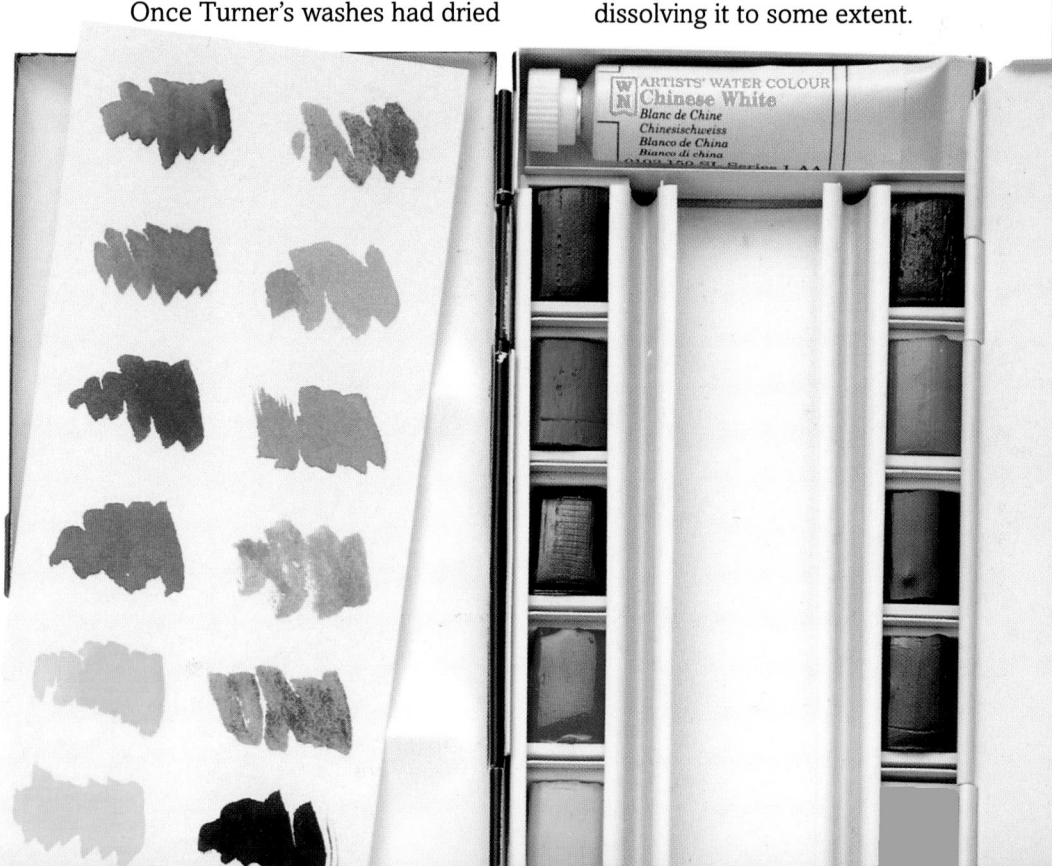

Paints and palettes
Saucers and paint box lids are just two of the many options for mixing paints. Painted colour swatches can provide a useful point of reference.

COLOUR MIXING

IT IS THEORETICALLY POSSIBLE to mix any colour you want from just three colours – red, yellow and blue – known as primary colours. In practice, however, it can be difficult to find pigments pure enough to do this, although a cool yellow, a crimson or bluish red and a pure, greenish blue will make good greens and good purples when mixed together.

Colour wheel

This wheel is based on the primary colours Winsor Blue, Permanent Rose and Cadmium Lemon. They have been selected because of their permanence and because they make lovely colours in combination. The colour wheel shows primary colours and secondary colours – secondaries being two primaries mixed together.

Secondary colours from Permanent Rose and Cadmium Lemon

Tertiary colours made from mixing all three primaries

OF THE THREE PRIMARIES, Permanent Red or Rose is a pure transparent colour on the crimson side of red. It mixes very well with the other primaries to make violets or oranges. Cadmium Lemon is not as transparent as the red but when it is reduced in washes it has a similar transparency on the paper.

Winsor Blue is a cool transparent blue with a high tinting strength and its purity of colour enables it to produce clean bright colours in mixtures. An alternative blue is French Ultramarine, which like Winsor Blue is very strong and can give deep toned washes. It produces a lovely purple with Permanent Rose, but because it is a reddish blue, the greens it produces with yellow are greyish. Mixes made from two primaries are known as secondaries.

Secondary colours from Winsor Blue and Permanent Rose

Tertiary colours made from mixing all three primaries

Tertiary colours made from mixing all three primaries

Secondary colours from Winsor Blue and Cadmium Lemon

PIGMENT QUALITIES

Pigments vary enormously in their particle size and weight. Manganese Blue is a heavy pigment and gives a very granulated wash while the highly diluted, lighter Winsor Green here has a streaky effect known as flotation.

Flotation

Granulation

There is no doubt that it is best to work, initially at least, with a limited palette (range of colours). On this page are a number of pigments that are all excellent and from which you might make your selection.

Reds and browns
Light Red and Venetian Red are warm orange/reds, and Indian Red is a lovely cool purplish red. Burnt Sienna is a transparent reddish brown while Raw Umber tends towards a greeny yellow, and Burnt Umber more towards a dark reddish brown.

Light Red
Venetian Red
Indian Red
Cadmium Red
Permanent Rose
Alizarin Crimson
Rose Madder
Burnt Sienna
Yellow Ochre
Raw Sienna
Raw Umber
Burnt Umber

Terre Verte
Oxide of Chromium
Winsor Green
Viridian

Greens
Terre Verte and Oxide of Chromium are permanent, low-key greens, Terre Verte being a transparent pigment and Oxide of Chromium being more opaque. Viridian is durable but weaker than Winsor Green.

Cobalt Blue
Cerulean Blue
Winsor Blue

Cobalt Violet
French Ultramarine

Blues
There are many permanent blues of which these are highly recommended.

Yellows
Yellow Ochre and Raw Sienna are useful earth pigments, as are the brighter and permanent Cadmiums.

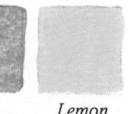

Yellow Ochre
Raw Sienna
Lemon Yellow Hue

Cadmium Yellow
Winsor Yellow
Cadmium Orange

Cadmium Lemon

Recommended palette
Your own palette or choice of colours will evolve naturally as you try out new colours and different kinds of painting, but these are some good ones to buy in terms of purity of colour, pigment strength and fastness to light. They also tend to work well in combination.

Cadmium Red *has good lightfastness and a little colour goes a long way.*

Permanent Rose *is a modern lightfast pigment which can replace the less durable Rose Madder.*

Cadmium Yellow *is bright and acceptably permanent and has a high tinting strength.*

Cadmium Lemon *is slightly paler than Cadmium Yellow and is equally permanent.*

Winsor Green *is both strong and permanent, mixing well with colours like Burnt Sienna.*

Winsor Blue *is also very permanent and has largely replaced the less lightfast Prussian Blue.*

French Ultramarine, *like Winsor Blue, is very strong and gives deep-toned washes.*

Burnt Sienna *is an earth pigment and so very durable. It has a lovely transparency.*

Raw Umber *is another very useful earth pigment and so will not fade over time.*

 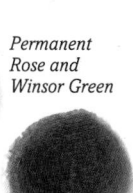

Permanent Rose and Winsor Green

Cadmium Red and Winsor Blue

MIXING GREYS
There are a number of colours which make lovely greys in combination, as shown on the left. For a much darker grey, mix Winsor Blue with Burnt Sienna. Black should be used with caution in watercolours and is not needed to make grey.

MIXING PRIMARIES

Orange
Two ways of arriving at a colour: left, laying one wash of colour over another; right, mixing colours in a tray before painting.

IN WATERCOLOUR TECHNIQUES there are essentially two ways of mixing colours – you can mix them physically in your mixing tray or you can mix them by laying one colour on top of another on the paper. In the first method you might add a small touch of blue to a yellow wash in your tray to create the colour green. In the second method, you can paint a yellow wash on to your paper, let it dry, and subsequently overpaint a pale blue wash to arrive at a green. Whichever painting method you use, the effect is essentially the same, although overlaying a wash of a second colour can, when done well, create a greater richness of hue. This is because your eyes should still be able to perceive the first colour reflected through the subsequent wash.

BOTH OF THESE FRUIT still lifes are painted by physically mixing three primary colours in a mixing tray before they are applied to the paper. The difference between the two versions is that the top one is painted with quite strong colours – what are known as high-key colours – while the bottom one is painted with muted or low-key colours.

Mixing colours

The mixing of two primary colours produces secondary colours, and the mixing of all three primary colours produces tertiary colours. Notice the range of colours that have been produced in each case with just three colours.

Range of colours produced from high-key primaries

High-key primaries
All the colours in this still life are created by mixing just three high-key primaries – Permanent Rose, Winsor Blue, and Cadmium Lemon. These colours produce a vast range of lovely hues, the swatches here being just a selection.

Range of colours produced from low-key primaries

Low-key primaries
This low-key study relies for its effects on mixing Indian Red, Cobalt Blue and Lemon Yellow Hue. These more muted versions of the three primaries work well in combination, producing subtle ranges of reds, oranges, greens and greys. The white highlights are created by the actual paper surface rather than by an application of colour.

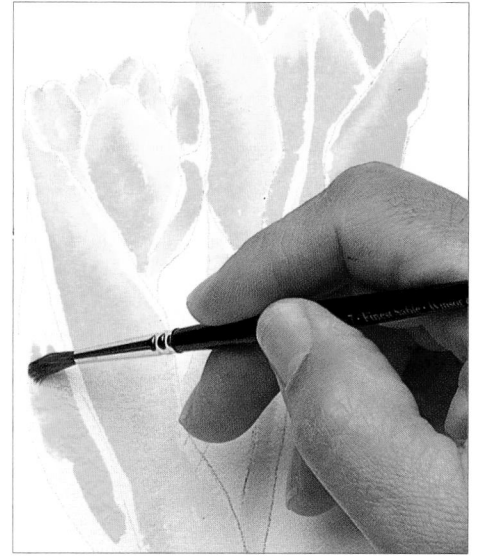

Overlaying colour
Here the tulips have been painted using three primaries, but the visual effects are created by overlaying washes of pure colour rather than by physically mixing the paint before applying it. Whichever way you choose to work, it is a good idea to do colour swatches on a scrap of similar paper in order to try out each colour on its own and also to see the effect when one colour is overlaid on to another, dried colour.

1 ◀ Starting with a pencil outline of the tulips, mix up a wash of Cadmium Lemon and begin applying it to the drawing with a small round brush. Paint in most of the leaves, the stem and the flowers, but be sure to omit any highlit areas which should appear white in the final image.

Cadmium Lemon

2 ◀ Allowing the yellow wash to dry, mix up a wash of Permanent Rose and test it on a dried swatch of the yellow to make sure that it produces the right kind of red. Now overlay your rose wash on the body of the petals.

Permanent Rose

The darkest areas of the petals have touches of Winsor Blue over the other two colours.

3 ◀ Again, allowing the paint to dry between layers, mix up some Winsor Blue and test it on a swatch of dried yellow. Using the tip of the brush, apply it to the darker areas of the stem and the leaves. Notice how the blue over the yellow creates an effective leaf-like green, even though no green has been applied.

The nature of overlaid colour is clearly visible in the stem and the leaves.

The blue wash is stronger and denser in certain areas and it is this which creates the shadows and gives the flower its three-dimensional form.

Ceramic palette

Winsor Blue

COLOUR HARMONY

CONSIDER THE BALANCE OF COLOURS in a painting. Are the colours bright and do they seem to shout at you, or are they low key and more subtle in their effect? If you are creating your own still life you have the advantage of being able to select particular items and arrange them in a variety of ways until you are happy with the result. You can manipulate not just what goes in to the painting in terms of shapes and textures, but exactly where everything goes. You can play with the composition to make it crowded or sparse, vibrant or muted. You can create a subtle balance in the range of colours or go more for primaries and secondaries. But whatever arrangement you choose, whether it is dark or light, high key and rich in colour or low key and subdued, you will find yourself instinctively striving for a sense of balance.

High key and low key
The contrast in colours between the vibrant, man-made objects of the beach ball and towels and the subdued, balanced tones of the pebbles and shells is striking. Here high key and low key are combined, the vibrancy of the stronger hues offsetting nature's more subtle offerings.

You can create interesting compositions by introducing bold primary colours into your still life.

Colours along the beach are generally low key – soft muted creams, yellows and browns.

IN JUGGLING THE ELEMENTS of sand, shells and towels you are making decisions about shapes, textures and colours. Nature abounds with colour, although along the seashore the colours are often muted as pebbles, shells, driftwood and sand provide a range of pale yellows and browns. But there are complementaries too – opposites on the colour wheel – so that the yellows are balanced by the purples of the seaweed; and also harmonious colours in which the tones or hues of colour are similar and work well together.

After-images
If we look at an area of strong colour for a long time and then look away at an area of white, we should perceive the complementary of the first colour. So that if we stare at an area of red and then look at a white wall we should, just for a moment, see a green shape. Similarly, if we focus on an orange-red colour first and then look at a bright yellow, we might see the yellow as green because we are carrying the blue after-image of the orange-red. These are the kinds of colour effects which we should bear in mind when planning a painting.

Low-key colours
Here shells, pebbles and starfish form a harmonious, low-key still life against the sand. The tones of the individual elements are roughly the same, with no single item vying for our attention.

Adjacent colours

Although technically the term adjacent colour means one that is next to another on the colour wheel, it is more commonly used to mean simply any colour which is next to another as, for example, in a painting. Every colour we use affects the appearance of the colour next to it. We can take advantage of this by painting with complementaries as adjacent colours. The colours will then appear brighter and will irradiate against each other.

For example, by putting orange/red next to violet it will appear more orange because the violet induces its complementary yellow. The same orange/red placed next to orange will look more blue because the orange induces its complementary blue. Many modern watercolour painters have used the technique of isolating colours from each other by leaving a white or grey gap between the touches of pure colour. This allows the individual colours to retain their clarity of hue.

Adjacent colours
The beach ball with its vibrant primary and secondary colours is offset by the equally strong towels. Note how the red of the ball reacts against its complementary green in the towel.

Isolated colours
The device of leaving unpainted edges around areas of bold colour serves to heighten the intensity of the individual colours.

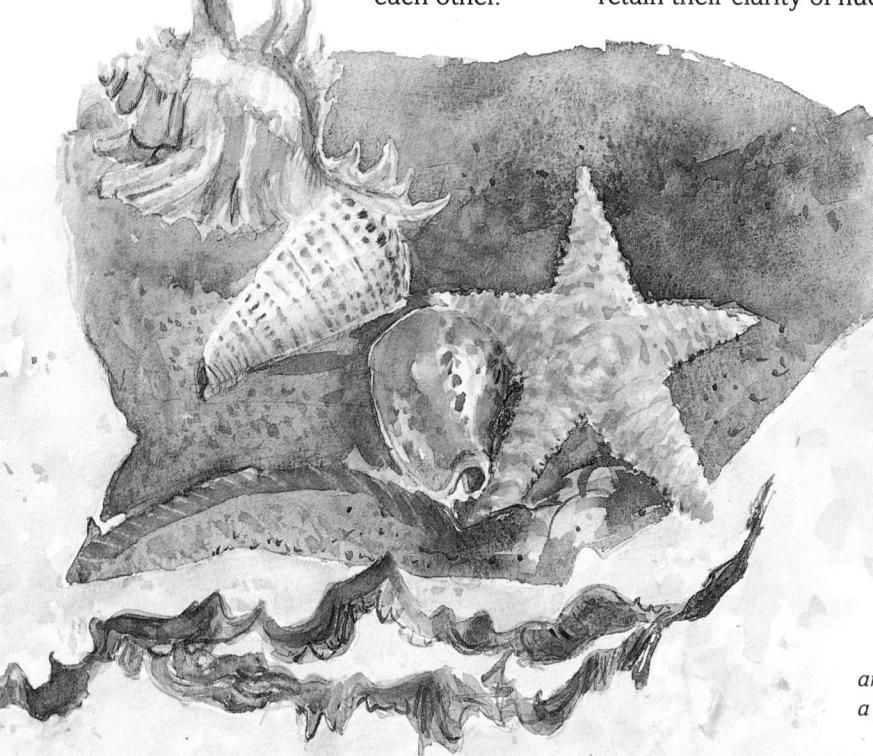

Complementary colours
This composition is one made up of complementary colours – yellows and purples, with the shells highlighted against the purple towel. Opposite each other on the colour wheel, complementary colours are mutually enhancing with each one of a pair intensifying the effect of the other.

19

LIGHT AND COLOUR

Warm lights / cool shadows

ONE OF THE MOST IMPORTANT aspects of watercolour painting is the way in which everything that we look at is affected by light, whether it be sunlight, moonlight or artificial light. It can be tempting to paint something a certain colour because that is the colour we know it to be, for example the pale yellow of sand on a beach. But at noon the sun could be so strong that the sand is virtually white, whereas in the late afternoon the sun may cast long, purplish shadows. You need to look carefully at the scene before you to consider the colour temperature of the light and how this affects the appearance of the ground on to which the shadows fall. A useful principle to follow is "warm lights/cool shadows", and conversely "cool lights/warm shadows". This principle holds good whatever the subject and however subtle the effects.

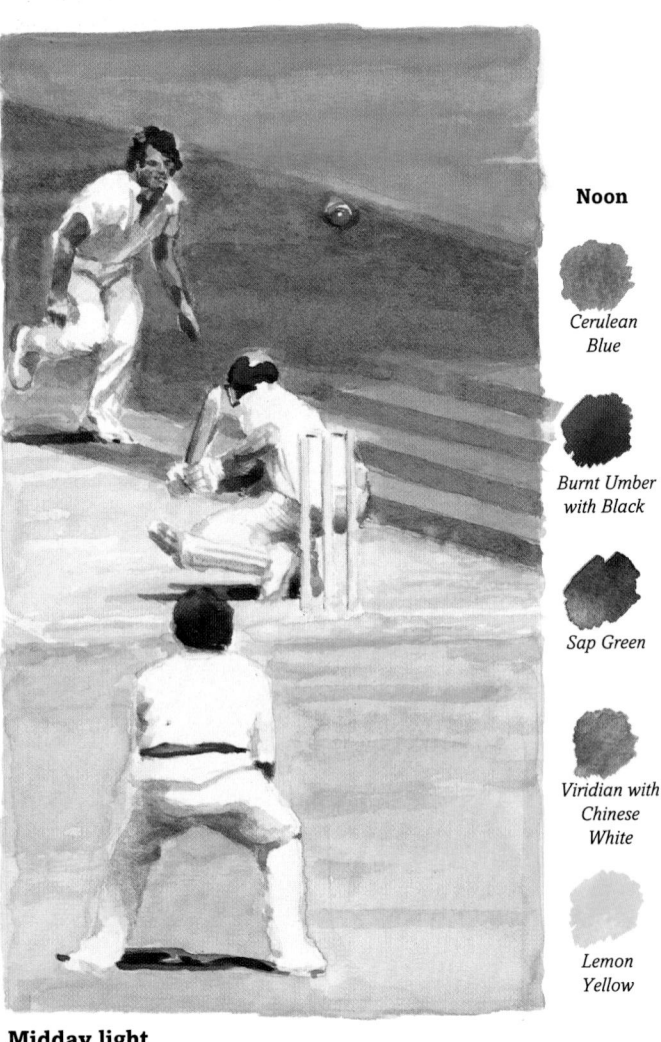

Noon

Cerulean Blue

Burnt Umber with Black

Sap Green

Viridian with Chinese White

Lemon Yellow

Midday light
At noon, when the sun is bright in a cloudless sky, we see lights and darks and very little in between. In the brightly lit areas the colour is washed out by the hard, cool light and the shadows are too dark to contain much colour. If, instead, the light from the sun is partially diffused by clouds, the shadows will be less pronounced and the colours will be more evident.

Evening

Hooker's Green

Cadmium Yellow

Ultramarine

Magenta

Evening light
In the evening when the sun is closer to the horizon and the light is less intense, the land can be bathed in a rich golden light. Here, a wash of Cadmium Yellow and Hooker's Green transform the colour of the grass while Magenta and Ultramarine give the bluish / purplish tinge to the cricketers' whites.

NOT ONLY DOES LIGHT affect the colours that we see but it gives form and life to shapes which might otherwise seem dull and flat. Objects in the foreground will be brighter and have more colour than those farther back, so in a case where you can see a panorama of tree-covered hills, the trees in the foreground will appear much brighter and more vibrant than those near the horizon. In terms of both what you see and how you paint it, a general guideline is that so-called warm colours advance towards you and cool colours recede. You can test this out when you paint by adding warm colours (such as orange/red) and cool colours (such as blue) and seeing which elements appear to advance and which appear to recede.

Monochromatic study
When you look at a landscape you will notice how the quality of light changes noticeably from the foreground to the background, markedly affecting all the colours that you perceive. By starting with a tonal study of the scene you can see quite clearly how the tones in the foreground are brighter and stronger than those in the background.

Chromatic study
In order to manipulate the way certain areas advance and recede in your painting, add warm colours such as yellows or reds to the foreground and cool colours to the background. Here you can see how the yellows have made the foreground trees stand out while the cool, bluish-purples which have been added to the distant hills make them appear even farther away.

Tinted acetate

Adjusting the colour
Painting in watercolours allows you to adjust the overall colour of your painting by laying a wash over it. You can, for example, make a painting warmer by overlaying a pale yellow wash over it or cooler by overlaying a pale blue wash. Here sheets of tinted acetate have been used to demonstrate the visual effects of overlaying warm and cool washes of colour. You will find that, depending on the time of day, the weather and the season when you are painting, you will need to adjust the intensity of the colours you use and the degree to which they seem warm or cool.

Although the painting is of a tropical landscape, the blue acetate makes the countryside seem almost English.

The central panel shows the actual painting, without any colour adjustments.

The pale yellow acetate has the effect of bathing the scene in a wash of golden sunlight.

GALLERY OF COLOUR

WATERCOLOUR IS A HIGHLY appropriate medium for exploring the effects of colour, as the pure colours of the pigments are seen in transparent washes against the white of the paper. Even when colours are overlaid, the translucent nature of the medium allows a subtle layering of colour. But equally, striking colour effects can be achieved by combining either high- or low-key colours within a painting.

Sue Sareen, *Daffodils*
Sareen favours a limited palette and this painting shows the effects that can be achieved with just a blue, a yellow and an ochre. Here she has worked with a very wet brush, allowing the background colours to merge while using the white of the paper to pick out the form of the flowers.

Philip O'Reilly, *San Giorgio at Dusk*
Painted as dusk set in, this striking image relies for its effect on the contrast between the dark solidity of the building against the intense blue of the evening sky. O'Reilly has used cream coloured paper to emphasize the warm hues of the Sicilian stonework and a granular blue-purple pigment to add texture and depth to the sky.

Paula Velarde, *Dining Room Brantwood*
Using candle wax to give a sense of texture, Velarde has overlaid bold washes of pigment with drier applications of colour, capturing the drama of the setting by counterpointing the blue with threads of an equally strong yellow. The hints of red in this predominantly blue scene serve to balance the overall effect.

The eye is drawn back and forth from the interior scene to the view from the window, with the bright red sailboat forming a point of interest in the lake.

Jane Gifford, *Tourist at Indian Wedding*
In this high-key study, the traveller paints a view of herself as she photographs the bride and groom at a wedding. Choosing a range of fluorescent colours to capture the heat and feel of her surroundings, Gifford emphasizes the strength of the sunlight by painting yellow highlights around herself and on the clothes of the wedding party.

Emil Nolde (attr.), *Ruttebüll Tief* (c.1916-20)
Here Nolde displays his characteristic celebration of colour, revelling in the power and purity of certain pigments. He has used washes of intense hue to create a highly personal non-naturalistic landscape. This vibrant painting demonstrates high-key colour at its most dynamic, with a perfect balance between adjacent and complementary colours and between the warmth of the central middle distance area and the unexpected and yet perfectly controlled coolness of the foreground.

BRUSHES

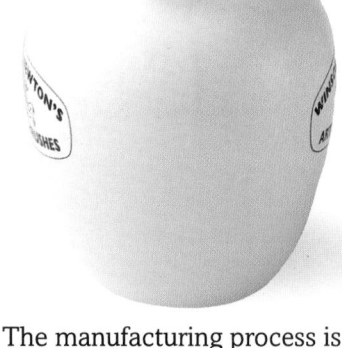

Earthenware vase for displaying brushes

THERE ARE TWO MAIN TYPES OF BRUSH, those with soft hairs, including red sable, ox hair, squirrel and polyester brushes, and those with harder hairs, the bristle brushes. Soft hair and synthetic brushes are the more traditional in watercolour painting techniques but bristle brushes are good for mixing up large amounts of colour and also in scrubbing out exercises.

THE ROUND SOFT HAIR BRUSHES, and in particular the sables, have been used to great effect in watercolour painting. They have excellent paint carrying capacity and they are springy and resilient. They come to a good point and can be used for fine work and also for laying in broader washes. Red sable is the tail hair of the Kolinsky, a species of mink. The soft woolly hairs are removed and only the strong resilient "guard" hairs used to make brushes. If you were to look at an individual hair through a microscope you would see that far from being smooth, it has a varying structure from root to tip which allows it to retain the paint. Each hair has a "belly" – a wider section in the middle – and consequently it tapers above and below. The belly forms spaces in the brush which act as reservoirs for the paint.

The hairs are of varying lengths between 25 and 60mm (1 – 2½ in). The long hairs are the rarest and the most prized and are around four times as expensive as the shorter ones.

Sable hairs

Ferrule

Sable brush

Anatomy of a brush
Brushes are made by hand, the lengths and quantity of the hairs being judged by eye.

The manufacturing process is all done by hand. The hair, which has previously been steamed under pressure and straightened, is put into a cannon, tapped and combed out to remove short hairs.

The blunt "white" hairs are removed and the correct quantity taken to make an individual brush. The amount is judged by eye as just enough to fit snugly into the ferrule – the metal tube connecting the hair and the handle.

Made by hand
In the smaller sizes, the hair comes to a point naturally. In the larger sables, the hair has to be turned or twisted to form the shape of the brush. It is then tied with a clove hitch knot, trimmed and cemented into the ferrule with epoxy resin for the larger sizes and shellac for the smaller sizes. The sable brushes are dipped into a weak gum arabic solution and individually sucked so that they come to a point.

CARE OF YOUR BRUSH

- It is good practice always to paint with two jars of water, one for rinsing the dirty brush in and the second for rinsing it again before mixing a new colour. This way you will keep your brush and your colours clean. When you finish painting, wash your brushes with soap to remove all traces of paint and then rinse them thoroughly. Do not use hot water for this, as it may expand the ferrule, soften the glue and make the hairs fall out.

- Brushes must be perfectly dry before being put away to avoid the possibility of mildew.

- You should keep your brushes clean and avoid building up deposits of paint at the ferrule as this has the effect of splaying the brush open and ruining the point.

- You can judge a round soft hair brush by its tip. A good one will always come to a point when dampened.

The toe (tip) of the brush

The heel of the brush

fill in the middle

The synthetic soft hair brushes are generally made from polyester monofilaments which, unlike the sable hairs, do not have a scale structure or surface irregularities. They tend to suck the paint up and also release it more quickly than the sables would. Generally, however, they are fine substitutes for sables. Manufacturers also produce brushes which combine natural and synthetic fibres in sable/polyester ranges. While they do not have the characteristic springiness of the pure sable they still do a perfectly reasonable job.

Round brushes
These come to a good point and, depending on the size, can be used for fine work or for laying in washes. The synthetic soft hair brushes and the synthetic/sable blends are fine for most manipulations, although less springy than the sables.

Wash brush
This mop-like wash brush is useful for laying down broad strokes of colour over large areas.

Flat wash brush
The flat one-stroke brush is good for toning paper or for laying a wash. It can also be used to modify a wash that has just been laid down.

Large wash brush
Useful for laying down very broad strokes of colour, this extra-wide wash brush comes into its own when covering large expanses of paper. The synthetic fibres have good paint-holding qualities and are excellent for laying washes and controlling the flow of paint.

Bamboo brush
Oriental soft-hair brushes are made of deer, goat, rabbit or wolf hairs.

Bristle brush
This hog hair brush is good for mixing up colour and also for scrubbing out techniques when it can be worked into the painted area with water. The shorter bristles aid control.

Size 3 sable

Size 6 sable

Size 12 sable/synthetic

Size 14b synthetic

1in sable/synthetic

2in synthetic

Japanese brush

Artist's hog hair short flat

25

BRUSHMARKS

BRUSHES CAN BE USED in a number of ways depending on the style or approach adopted by the artist. They can be used vigorously and expressively, for instance, to create brushstrokes of great energy and immediacy, or they can be used simply as the invisible tool that allows a wash to be applied evenly within a prescribed area. Between the two lies a world of different approaches. Factors which come into play are the amount of paint in the brush, the speed of the stroke, the angle of the brush and the type of brush being used. The nature of the paper will also play a part. These pages show the variety of brushstrokes that can be made using just one brush.

Brushmarks from a single brush
All the strokes on these pages are made with a size 9 sable.

With a well loaded brush, gradually increase the pressure until the full width of the brush comes into play.

Using lumps of pan paint, apply them to the paper with a very wet brush.

Using the tip of the brush in a circular motion, gradually increase the pressure to use more and more of the brush hairs.

A thin line can be drawn by just using the tip of the brush.

Rotate the side of the brush in a circular motion.

Sponge the paper first and then press the brush down firmly on to the dampened surface.

Roll a fully loaded brush on its side in complete revolutions.

The tip of the brush can draw fine dots and outlines.

THIS SIMPLE PAINTING puts into practice some of the strokes that can be made with a single brush, again using a size 9 sable. It is all a matter of control and of getting to know the nature of the brush, the paint and the paper.

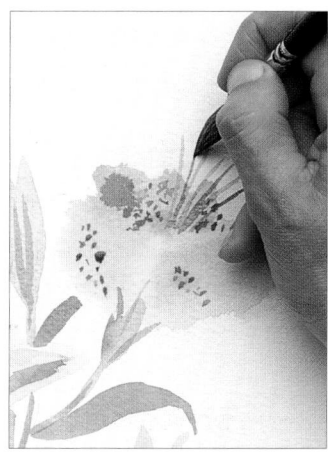

1 ▲ Wash in broad petal shapes with the body of the brush using Rose Madder and a touch of Ultramarine. Then with a stronger mix, use the tip of the brush to dot in colour. Where the petals are still wet the dots will bleed.

2 ▲ Draw the stem in a thin line using a mix of Rose Madder, Ultramarine, Sap Green, Viridian, Yellow Ochre and Winsor Blue. Then, pressing harder on the brush, complete each leaf with a single brushstroke.

3 ▲ Using the finest point of the brush, draw in the filaments using Sap Green. If you are worried about not being able to control these fine lines, do a few practice ones on a rough scrap of paper before you begin, keeping your hand as steady as possible.

4 ▲ The anthers at the end of the filaments are Indian Red painted in dry brushstrokes. The combination of the paint applied in this way on to dry paper creates a sense of depth and texture.

For fine lines just the tip of the brush comes into play.

To create a sense of depth, the background is painted in with a very dilute Yellow Ochre applied in broad brushstrokes.

You can make lines as fine as these with a size 9 brush by having just a touch of paint on the longest hairs.

The shadow from the vase is created by using the full body of the hairs to apply the paint both wet and dry.

The patterned surface is achieved by dipping the brush into a thick mixture of Winsor Blue and Ultramarine, and then rolling the brush repeatedly on its side.

OTHER MARKS

ALTHOUGH PAINT BRUSHES are the tools which are traditionally used for applying paint and which are essential for a vast range of techniques, there are nevertheless many alternative methods for applying watercolour paint on to your paper. It is largely a matter of trying out different implements and seeing which you prefer and which get closest to the effects you are after. But you do not have to buy lots of expensive equipment – there are any number of ordinary household items that you can experiment with. Artists have used such diverse materials as pieces of cardboard, sponges, wallpaper brushes, combs, paint rollers and even squeegees in order to achieve interesting effects. You will need to try different dilutions of paint and various types of paper to achieve the best results.

This spigotted bamboo brush with its mix of animal hairs creates broad, loose brushstrokes.

Blotting paper is used here. First apply paint with a brush. Then dip an edge of torn blotting paper into wet paint and press it down. Draw the blotting paper along to create the pattern.

Dip an old sponge in masking fluid, press it on to the paper and let it dry. Paint over it and while the paint is still wet, lift it off with a tissue.

Dip one edge of the cardboard in some paint and drag it in vertical or horizontal strokes.

Cardboard
The gate has been painted with cardboard while the grassy effects are the result of sponging.

Cow gum eraser
Gradually build up a ball of cow gum. It will have a mottled, uneven texture. Dip it into some paint and press it on to your paper. Repeat the process with other colours.

Old brushes have their uses. Here a worn, splayed brush has been dipped into a pale blue-grey wash and used to paint this tree.

This tree is painted with a fine sable brush. There is more control, particularly in the trunk, than can be achieved with the splayed brush.

The rigger with its characteristic long, fine hairs is capable of perfectly controlled lines and so is good for more detailed work.

Dip a natural sponge in masking fluid and apply it lightly to the paper. After it has dried, paint a wash of violet over it.

Use a comb for this effect. First paint the two colours in turn and while each is still wet, draw the comb across the paint to create the blades of grass.

Sold in most artist supply shops, this small sponge roller is good for laying strips of colour. The tone will vary depending on how much paint the sponge has absorbed and how hard you press down on it.

Natural sponge

The leaves are painted by dipping a sponge in light green and then dark green, and pressing it down on the paper. The irregular surface of the sponge creates interesting textures. For the trunk, dip the sponge in brown, squeeze it and draw it down the page.

GALLERY OF BRUSHSTROKES

ONE OF THE PLEASURES of watercolour painting is that you really only need a couple of good quality brushes to get started – a small round pointed sable for detailed work and a bigger, soft-hair round brush for washes and larger effects. Sables, with their characteristic springiness, are the traditional watercolour brush, but there are any number of excellent alternatives to choose from including synthetic hair brushes and synthetic/sable mixes.

Julian Gregg, *Dieppe Harbour, Summer*
This study comprises a series of solid brushstrokes corresponding to areas of buildings in shadow and their reflections. Here the simple fluent line drawing was the essential starting point for the straightforward and economical brushstrokes. Gregg relied on just one or two brushes and a limited palette of colours, allowing the brushstrokes to remain clearly visible in the finished work. He built up the work swiftly and confidently, starting with the light areas and ending with the darkest reflections in the water.

Ian Cook, *Head of a Girl*
The intense colour of the highly pigmented gouache shows in the thicker, dense brushstrokes, especially in the face and neck. The brushwork here is closer in feel to that of an oil painting with its rich, impasto effect.

John Pike, *Number 10 Fournier Street*
The artist worked from photos, sketches and colour notes to arrive at this degree of realism. The brushwork is relatively invisible so that nothing detracts from the final image. Pike built up the painting gradually, starting with overall washes and then filling in the details with a fine brush.

Raoul Dufy, *Nice, Le Casino*, 1936
This lovely loose study perfectly illustrates the artist's control over brushwork, with the figures, trees and outlines of the building fluently touched in with the toe of a pointed, round, soft-hair brush.

These rapid and assured touches, balanced by the broader brushstrokes of some of the palm trees, are painted over sweeping washes of pinks, lilacs and blues. The outlines of the buildings are similarly drawn in a wide range of colours.

Gisela Van Oepen,
The Sun Sets Behind the Tree
Painted with confidence, the brushstrokes here are clearly visible, from the diagonal sweeps of the sky to the large frilly strokes used for the branches.

The bright rectangle in the lower left-hand corner of the window is light coming through from the far side of the building. Using a fine pointed brush, Pike painted carefully around this area so that it is actually the paper rather than any paint which creates this bold shaft of light.

PAPER

WATERCOLOUR ARTISTS REQUIRE paper in varying weights, of a quality that will not yellow with age and with a range of surface types from smooth to rough. The paper should not buckle once it has been stretched and needs to be sufficiently strong to withstand quite severe treatment. Additionally, it ought to have the right degree of absorbency for the kind of painting the artist has in mind.

Oriental sketchbooks
Unusual papers provide interesting textured surfaces.

PAPER IS PRODUCED by the felting together of cellulose fibres obtained from a variety of plant sources. In the West, most artists' papers are now produced from cotton fibres while Oriental papers are made from a great variety of plant sources. These have fibres of varying length and strength which impart very different characteristics to each type of paper.

The first stage of manufacture is the pulping stage, during which the material providing the fibres is blended with water to produce a slurry. This is beaten

Cylinder mould machine
Here the pulped fibres are drawn over a wire mesh, arranging themselves in a random order.

and refined in order to produce fibres of the requisite quality. A neutral internal sizing is then added to the pulp. This, together with the additional surface sizing which may be added later, controls the absorbency of the paper.

Most watercolour papers are not nowadays made by hand but on a cylinder mould machine. From here the paper passes through a press on a woollen felt or blanket which gives it a rough or a fine grain surface depending on the weave used for the felt. The paper is still very wet so it is

Waterford Rough

Waterford NOT

Waterford Smooth

Winsor & Newton Smooth

Winsor & Newton NOT

Bockingford White NOT

Bockingford Grey NOT

Bockingford Oatmeal NOT

Mould-made paper
These are all standard machine-made watercolour papers. Note how the different surfaces affect the appearance of the paint, the blue looking much darker on the toned paper and much grainier on the Rough sheet at the back.

passed through a press and then round drying cylinders to remove the excess water. The paper is subsequently immersed in warm gelatine for surface sizing before being passed through squeeze rollers and dried. The function of the gelatine sizing is to decrease the paper's absorbency and make it harder. It allows it to withstand severe treatment such as constant repainting and scrubbing off.

Absorbency

This is determined by the amount of size used in the manufacture of the paper. (You can quite easily add a coat of gelatine size to make your paper harder and less absorbent.) A paper with no size is known as Waterleaf. Many of the Oriental papers are very absorbent, taking up the brushstroke as it is made and not allowing any further manipulation.

Acidity is another factor which you should consider. It is always preferable to use acid-free paper with a neutral pH. This ensures that the paper will not darken excessively with age.

Unusual papers
Oriental papers such as the top two are made from plant sources. Toned papers have a vegetable dye added to them.

Weight
This is measured in pounds per ream (480 sheets) or grammes per square metre. Light, thin papers can be soaked through if that is the desired effect and can also be quite strong. Really heavy papers do not need stretching and so are ideal for vigorous painting techniques.

90lb

140lb

260lb

300lb

board

Blocks and pads
Watercolour paper can be bought in loose sheets, in spiral-bound pads and in blocks. The blocks, which are bound on all four sides, have the advantage that the paper does not need to be stretched before painting.

Hot-pressed or Smooth surface   *NOT or Cold-pressed surface*   *Rough surface*

Surface and weight

The three standard grades of surface in Western papers are Rough, HP (Hot-pressed) and NOT (Cold-pressed). Rough is just as its name suggests, a rough surface. Hot-pressed comes out very smooth, and NOT or cold-pressed is a fine-grain or semi-rough surface – literally "not hot pressed". These categories vary enormously from one manufacturer to another, so look at several types before deciding which to buy. In terms of weight, both light and heavy papers have their advantages; it is largely a question of what you want to paint and which particular techniques you plan to use.

STRETCHING AND TONING

WATERCOLOUR PAPER needs to be stretched in advance to ensure that it does not cockle and buckle when you are painting on it but stays firm and flat on the drawing board. The procedure is quite simple: all you need is a board, some gum strip, a sponge and water. Once your paper has been stretched you may want to tone it. Although you can buy toned paper, toning it yourself creates a somewhat different effect since you are in fact laying a transparent colour over white paper. Also, it allows you to create any colour you desire.

Unstretched paper

Stretching paper

Unless you are going to use blocks of watercolour paper or very heavy paper, you should always stretch your paper before you start painting. You need to get hold of a board which is several centimetres wider than your paper on all four sides. It should be thick enough to withstand the tensions of the stretched paper without bending and it should be slightly absorbent. Plywood, chipboard, blockboard or medium density fibreboard all make good surfaces and can be purchased cheaply from any timber merchant.

Materials for stretching

Sponges

Gum strip

Fibreboard
Chipboard
Plywood

1 ▲ Start by preparing four strips of heavy duty gummed brown paper of the right length, one for each side of the paper, and put them to one side. Next, wet your sheet of paper thoroughly with cold water to allow the fibres to expand. Don't use hot water as this might remove the gelatine surface sizing of the paper.

2 ▲ Make sure the whole sheet is uniformly damp. You can wet the paper with a moist sponge or immerse it in a bath of cold water for a few minutes, depending on the thickness of the paper. Once the paper has expanded, moisten your lengths of gum strip with a sponge. If they are too wet they will not stick properly.

3 ▲ When your paper is thoroughly wetted, put it on to the drawing board, smooth it out, and sponge off any excess water. Next, take the gummed brown tape and stick the paper down firmly around the edges.

4 ▲ Now let the paper dry. You can speed up the process by using a hair-drier on a low setting if you wish. When the water evaporates, the paper fibres contract and the paper becomes hard and flat.

Toning paper

Most watercolour paper is white. While this suits those techniques which rely on the brightness of the ground to reflect light back through the colour, the history of watercolour painting is full of works created on paper of widely varying tones. There are several advantages to toning paper yourself – it allows you to experiment with a wide range of different coloured grounds for your painting and also simple studies will look quite finished, the colour of the paper serving to unify the whole. One difficulty, however, is the problem of re-solubility – if you tone your paper with watercolour paint, you risk dislodging the colour when you paint on it. Using well diluted acrylic paints for toning will eliminate this risk.

Materials for toning

Acrylic paint

1½ inch wash brush

1 ▲ Mix up sufficient paint – in this case well diluted acrylics – to cover the whole sheet. Apply the mix using a large brush with the board at a slight angle to the horizontal. Pick up any drips with each successive brushstroke. The secret to toning paper evenly is to work quickly, making smooth horizontal brushstrokes.

2 ▲ Be sure to let your paper dry thoroughly before painting on it. The reason for using acrylics rather than watercolours for toning is that there is a slight danger that a watercolour base might dissolve when you paint over it. Acrylic paint will not be re-soluble after it has dried and so will be fine to paint on.

Painting on toned paper
Although sketchy, the still life has quite a finished appearance due to the coloured background. The artist has painted on the blue acrylic toned paper, using watercolours for the darker areas and white gouache for the highlights.

See how much lighter the background is once the paint has dried. You will need to allow for this when you tone paper yourself, whether you are using a watercolour base or an acrylic one.

The use of gouache for the highlights on the two fish and on the mushrooms is particularly effective. Pale watercolours would get lost against the strength of the background.

GALLERY OF PAPER

THE WAY YOUR WATERCOLOUR PAINTING looks is conditioned as much by the paper you paint on as by the way that you paint. A weakly-sized absorbent paper will give a completely different look to the same manipulation applied to a hard, surface-sized paper. The texture of the paper will similarly affect the appearance of the paint, with a rough surface giving a more textured look than a smooth, hot-pressed surface as the heavier pigments settle into the dips and hollows of the paper. Another factor to consider is the colour of the paper. Indeed, the use of toned paper opens up a whole new range of possibilities including the use of body colour for highlights and a more overall low-key approach.

Although the paper is made by hand, there is nevertheless a regularity to the pattern which shows in the finished image.

The texture of the paper absorbs some of the paint and encourages a certain degree of bleeding of colours.

Jane Gifford, *Gathering Weed on Nagin Lake*
Painted on rough handmade Indian paper, the water in this Kashmiri scene appears slightly choppier than that in the similar study at the right.

Sharon Finmark, *Portrait of Lia*
Many watercolour painters who enjoy the traditional transparent use of the medium tend to avoid toned paper, believing that it will adversely affect the appearance of the colour. But as with this sensitive study, the buff toned paper actually creates a subtler and more effective backdrop than would a white ground. So in the areas that have been left unpainted, both to frame the girl and to act as highlights, it is the warmth of the paper that serves to harmonize and unify the whole.

Paul Klee, *Das Schloss*, c.1925
Throughout his life, Paul Klee was fascinated by the materials and techniques of painting and his work reflects that interest. His constant experimentation with watercolours made him acutely sensitive to the innate quality of each new colour and to the texture of a particular

Jane Gifford, *Two Shikaras on Nagin Lake*
This sketch, done on location in Kashmir, seems altogether more peaceful than the one on the left. Gifford uses the smooth surface of the paper to emphasize both the clearness of the sky and the glasslike quality of the water as the boats glide along its surface.

Here the unsized paper dictates the nature of the painting, creating a typically Chinese effect. The washes of paint are absorbed immediately into the paper but even the ink lines, applied lightly with a fine drawing nib, bleed the moment the ink touches the paper.

piece of paper. It was factors such as these which led to the unique quality of his vision and his painting. Absolutely integral to the feel of this image is the heavy laid texture of the paper. The paint settles in its hollows and the scene is given a rough, grainy feel. The strong, scratchy ink line is the web holding this image together.

Jane Gifford, *Near Yangshuo, China*
An absorbent paper can give a softer, more diffused look than a hard, surface-sized paper. This Chinese handmade paper automatically creates a Chinese-style painting. The quality of the paper prevents techniques such as washing off or masking.

WAYS OF WORKING

IT IS USEFUL TO HAVE a certain amount of knowledge about the tools and materials of watercolour because this allows you to make appropriate decisions about which colours to use, for example, or which type of paper would be best in a given situation. But far more than this you need to practise working with watercolour so that you get a real feel for the medium rather than just understanding it intellectually.

Two basic brushes

An image made with a cow gum rubber

Gaining confidence

Essentially, the art of watercolour painting is about developing an ability to allow the paint to do its own thing while at the same time remaining in control of the process. Gradually you will start to recognise what is going on in your painting and will respond to it instinctually. What begins as a somewhat self-conscious process, as you attempt to make the right decisions about your painting – what colours to use, the degree of dilution, the type of brush and so on – ends by becoming a much more intuitive one. You will start to recognise what your painting needs at any given moment without necessarily having to think about it. And with experience you will know both what particular colours or techniques are called for and also be able to put that knowledge into practise.

Controlling the medium

At its more complex, the watercolour medium can be extremely testing because it relies on such a high degree of control. It involves control over the amount and density of paint in the brush, control over how the brush applies the paint to the wet or dry surface of the painting and control in modifying and moving the paint around on that surface. Many of the techniques which are associated with watercolour require the rapid and spontaneous application of colour, and in some instances there is

Softening details with a natural sponge

only one opportunity to get it right if the whole thing is not to be washed off under cold water and begun again. But it also provides opportunities for artists who wish to create complex works involving, for example, building-up layer on layer of thin washes of colour using small and precise brushstrokes. In addition, there are a number of specialist techniques such as "stopping out" (*see* pp.60-61) and "wax resist" (*see* pp.62-3), in which different materials and skills are used in a painting to retain the original colour of the paper or of a previous wash.

Masking fluid and a dip pen

Crumpled paper towel

Natural sponge

Cow gum rubber

Toothbrush

Scalpel

A simple process

In general, however, the materials and techniques of watercolour are straightforward. For the most part, both beginner and professional are simply using watercolour paints mixed with water for all their manipulations. Most techniques are variations on a basic repertoire which involves the laying of washes, working wet-into-wet and painting in layers. In the next section of our *Introduction to Watercolour* we look at these various ways of working, starting with the basics of pencil sketches, drawing and composition and moving on to the application of washes, the building up of colour in layers, and the more advanced techniques of resist (*see* pp.60-63) and s'graffito (*see* pp.58-9).

Reaping the benefits

It may take time and practice to learn these skills so that the paint does what you want it to do and expect it to do, but the medium is rewarding right from the start. You will soon discover that watercolours can provide a satisfying and versatile challenge, as much to the beginner as to the more advanced artist.

Sandpapered surface

CAPTURING AN IMAGE

APART FROM MAKING PENCIL SKETCHES, artists today have a range of mechanical devices with which to record a scene, from simple drawing frames to cameras, camcorders or slide projectors. Artists can project slides on to a screen and trace them or colour copy photographs, enlarging those areas that most interest them.

Zoom lenses

Many cameras now have zoom facilities or wide-angle lenses so that you can get very close to a scene or record a much wider area, depending on what you want to record.

Drawing frame

You can use a drawing frame as a viewfinder, dividing the scene in front of you into manageable sections and then copying the grid on to a sheet of paper to guide you. You can make your own drawing frame by outlining a grid on to a sheet of acetate.

Masking out

There may be details in your photo which you wish to exclude, in which case the simplest method is to mask them out. Here the artist wants to focus on the two girls with the rabbit and so has "framed" the area she is interested in.

Here the artist has masked out superfluous details on the photo

Colour photocopies

The advantage of working from a photograph is that you can make a colour copy of your print and then enlarge it (or a section of it) without losing quality. The larger of the two copies below has been blown up to 400 per cent.

Tracing paper

If you lack the confidence to draw your image freehand, you can trace it from a photo. To tranfer it to your paper, copy the lines on to the back of the tracing paper, place it on your sheet and rub over the pencil lines.

THERE ARE NO RULES about how you should start your painting. If you feel sufficiently confident, you can do a pencil drawing directly on to your sheet of paper, or even start painting immediately. But if you prefer to work from a photograph, or even to trace an image on to your paper before you start, that is also fine. For centuries artists have used whatever aids were at their disposal. Albrecht Dürer *(1471-1528)* illustrated a framed grid as a drawing device and Vincent Van Gogh *(1853-90)* had a portable grid made up for him by a blacksmith. Today, with all the technological advances that have been made, there are even more tools to play with.

VIDEO CAMERAS

Artists of today can use home video cameras to record scenes they might wish to paint later. Often the camera lens sees more clearly than the eye, having the facility to take close-ups and focus in on the smallest of details. Depending on the type of camera, films can then be projected on to a screen or run through a television screen. Either way, it is generally possible to freeze-frame a scene and then trace or copy it on to a sheet of paper. You can then enlarge or reduce your image by using the grid method outlined below.

The grid method

This is the means of transferring an image on to your paper. You can either draw a grid of squares on to your original or on to a sheet of acetate which you place over your original. You then draw an identical grid on to your sheet of paper, although it may be considerably larger if you want to scale the image up. You can then refer to the grid on the original and plot the outlines square by square on to your paper.

Ruler and pencil

Painting by numbers

By numbering along one side of your grid and putting letters down the other, you can more easily plot your picture. Detailed areas of the original may need more squares. Here, for example, the girls' faces have more squares to make it easier to paint them.

COMPOSITION

KNOWING HOW BEST TO COMPOSE your painting is often surprisingly difficult, but there are some guidelines that are worth following. The position of the horizon line is critical. Looking down from a high vantage point will give you a high horizon line and consequently you will be able to map out the whole landscape or seascape like a carpet on your painting. A low horizon line which allows you to look up at the scene in front of you gives you an opportunity to make the most of the sky. It also means that large objects in the foreground will have the effect of towering above you. It is best to place points of visual interest slightly off-centre, and to avoid placing the horizon line right through the middle of the painting.

THE POSITIONING OF the main features of your composition does not have to follow a particular pattern, but artists generally try to achieve a sense of balance. This can be done intuitively on the basis that if it feels right it probably is right. Such a balance can emerge from the fact that tones are deeper in the foreground and become progressively lighter towards the horizon. Or the sense of balance might be due to the relative weight of certain features in the painting. For example, an artist might feel that the massive shape of a tree on the left needs to be balanced by something on the right.

Focal point

An alternative composition would be to place a large object such as a tree on a point off-centre to right or left, planted low but extending almost to the top edge. This would provide a focus or a pivot from which the rest of the composition would flow. If you look at such a painting and rearrange the edges with pieces of white card so that the tree is right in the centre, you will see how much less subtle it is.

Sketching in pencil

A vast panorama
Here the artist wanted to capture the vastness of the scene in front of her. The focal point of the hilltop village is slightly off-centre and the rooftops lead the viewer in a meandering line, from foreground to background.

Playing with perspective
It is generally best to avoid placing the horizon line right through the middle of your painting. In the example above, the sky detracts from the points of interest whereas the low vantage point in the view on the right is far more dramatic.

OPEN AND CLOSED COMPOSITIONS

In an open composition the scene that you see is clearly part of a larger scene, while in a closed one what you see is all there is, like looking at a fish tank. Most compositions have elements of both. The important thing is not to let a key element of your composition slide off the page.

Closed composition *Open composition*

The final painting

The artist selected this view for her finished painting, opting for the high horizon line to capture the sense of the village reaching heavenwards. There is virtually no sky and we are drawn up and down the scene in an upside-down "V" shape as we follow the line of the rooftops up and the trees back down again.

Here there is both a visual harmony in the balance of shapes and forms and a colour harmony in the balance of reds to greens. The background hills provide a resting point for the eye.

A sense of balance

In this composition the artist has placed the focal point of the village slightly to the right of centre with the horizon line in the middle of the page. Although a centered horizon is something which should generally be avoided, it is not oppressive in this case because of the lightness of the sky. The viewer is led from the distant building on the summit of the hill, across the rooftops to the left of the page, and then on towards the nearest roof on the right. We are poised above the roof looking out. The artist has achieved a sense of balance in the colours she has chosen as well as with the positioning of the scene.

Shifting to the left

Here the points of interest are on the left-hand side of the painting. The horizon line has been moved up so the sense of perspective is somewhat distorted as we look both down on the foreground buildings and up at the ones in the distance. The sun-drenched hills on the right tend to be more of a distraction than a harmonious counterpoint to the village.

DRAWING

DRAWING AND SKETCHING are an integral part of watercolour painting. Armed with just a sketchbook and a pencil, you can record the main features of a scene swiftly or in greater detail. You can make notes about the particular colours and tones if you are going to translate your sketch into a painting later. Whatever your chosen method, making initial drawings gives you the space to reflect on what the focus of your painting should be, and will tell you fairly quickly if something is going to work well as a final composition.

Conté crayon
Available in varying degrees of hardness, conté crayon comes in a range of colours including black, white and red. Less powdery than chalk, it still needs fixing before applying a wash. Fixatives come in spray cans.

Charcoal
One of the oldest drawing materials, charcoal is very powdery and must be sprayed with a fixative to prevent it smudging or mixing with the overlaid watercolour – unless this happens to be the desired effect.

Smooth paper

Rough paper

Conté crayon

Charcoal

Pencil

Graphite stick

Reed pen and ink

Drawing materials
The tool that you choose to work with depends on your subject matter, on the effects that you want to achieve and on personal preference. Pencils are easy to rub out if you make a mistake while graphite sticks, which are in essence fat pencil leads, are better for shading. In these examples the marks have been drawn on the paper and then overlaid with the wash. Note the different effects on the two surfaces and also how the charcoal has mingled with the paint. Still other effects occur if you dampen the surface first.

A PENCIL DRAWING can serve a variety of purposes and different kinds of pencil are appropriate in each case. The traditional sketching pencil has a soft, fat lead which is good for tonal studies, but if you are making an essentially linear drawing you might prefer a clutch pencil with a relatively thin (.5mm) lead no softer than about a B. Artists soon develop their own way of making drawings, but if you are not used to making pencil sketches, practise by making drawings of some small, simple objects. Before you begin, try to see the outline of the whole thing and then look to see how various lines and curves within the overall shape define the kind of object it is. It is best to start on a small scale before embarking on a larger picture.

Pencil drawing

Pencil and wash

Pencil sketch
The artist did several sketches of her cat before settling on this particular pose. She tried it from different angles and with certain background details and decided that this simple study from a slightly raised perspective was the most successful.

Ink drawing

Pen and wash
These two figures work well both as a simple pen and ink drawing and with the washes of watercolour. The latter has a greater solidity to it but the line drawing has its own charm. Most drawing inks will not run or dissolve once they are dry so there should be no problem in putting layers of paint over an ink sketch.

Ink and wash

DRAWING NIBS

There are many types of steel nibs which you can use for drawing – it is largely just a matter of personal preference. There are the standard drawing nibs and then the script pen nibs which can also be used. These come in a variety of widths, with or without reservoirs. They all have a springiness in the steel which allows the artist to vary the width and the quality of the line while drawing. Mapping nibs are good for very fine lines, while italic nibs can be either fine or broad.

Italic nib   *Mapping nib*   *Script nib*   *Drawing nib*

LAYING A WASH

A WASH IS A THIN LAYER of watercolour paint which is usually applied with a well charged brush over a fairly large area. It can be applied on to dry or damp paper, or it can be overlaid on to dry colour already on the paper.

The wash can be manipulated wet, so that particular areas can be lifted and lightened, or other colours can be dropped into it while it is still wet. Alternatively, the wash can be adapted in various ways when it is dry.

How to lay a flat wash

1 ◀ Mix up enough paint before you begin and make sure it is well stirred. You cannot stop halfway through to mix up more. It is a good idea to use a bristle brush for mixing the paint as this will break it down more easily. Then for applying the wash, use a soft hair brush; either round or flat is fine.

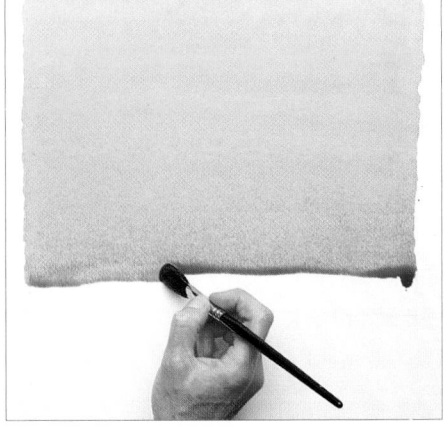

2 ▶ With a well charged wash brush, keep a continuous line of wet colour forming along the bottom edge. You may find it easier if the paper is at a slight angle. It is also easier to apply a flat, uniform wash on to a NOT or Rough surface than on to a smooth one since the smooth surface will show up any streaks.

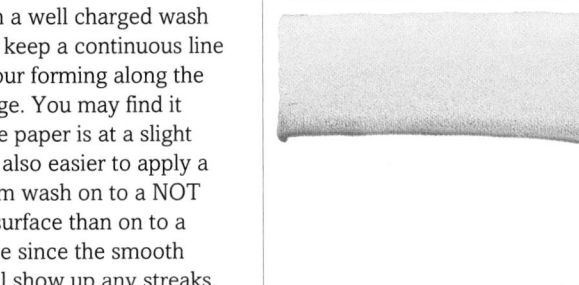

3 ▲ Pick up the paint with each succeeding stroke. Try to avoid any trickles, and apply the paint in a smooth, continuous motion. You can work left to right and/or right to left.

Flat wash
This doorway has been created with washes of flat colour, in this case a very dilute mix of Cobalt Blue and Permanent Rose. Note the granulation of the pigment on the NOT (semi-rough) surface.

**Graded
one-colour wash**
A graded wash is one in which the tone moves smoothly from dark to light. Mixing a light, a mid and a dark tone of orange in separate saucers, apply the darkest tone first and proceed down the page.

Laying a variegated wash

1 ▲ To help the wash flow out you can wet the area to be painted first with a sponge or a brush. Then with a soft hair wash brush, either round or flat, apply your wash of Winsor Blue to the paper.

3 ▲ Working fairly fast on to the wet surface, apply some loose brushstrokes of Lemon Yellow in the right-hand corner.

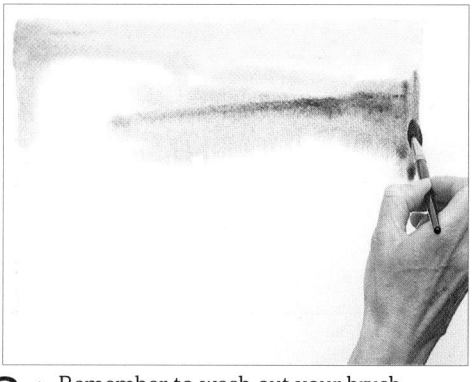

2 ▲ Remember to wash out your brush between colours. Then, starting at the right-hand side, wash in some Violet, touching the Blue in parts and allowing the Violet to diffuse across the page.

TIPS

● Mix up enough paint before you begin and make sure the mixture remains well stirred since many pigments have a tendency to settle in the saucer.

● It is a good idea to mix your wash colour with a different brush to the one with which you apply it. A bristle brush is best if you are mixing a fair amount of paint from a tube as you can break the paint down into a well diluted mix more easily than with a soft hair brush.

● Many artists like to work with their paper at an angle when applying washes as this allows them to control the flow of the paint more easily.

● To achieve a more uniform tone you can dampen your paper before you apply your wash.

● Remember that a watercolour wash dries lighter in tone than it appears when you paint it on, so you should compensate for this in your mix.

4 ◀ Here some areas of Carmine are added at the bottom. All the paints have been applied very wet and the board has been moved around to allow the colours to flow in particular directions. Note how the different pigments react with each other and also with the surface of the paper.

Graded two-colour wash

Running one tone into another can be done with two or more colours. Mix sufficient quantities of the colours you require and apply them swiftly, allowing them to mingle and diffuse if you wish.

Variegated wash

To wash several colours over areas of your painting, pre-mix the colours and then paint them quite rapidly up to the boundary of the neighbouring colour. The colours will then diffuse into each other along the join.

WASHES

WASHES WILL VARY depending on the pigments used, on how they are applied and also on the quality of the paper. For example on smooth paper there is a tendency for washes to appear streaky, while on a rough surface they may not penetrate into the hollows of the paper. But washes can also be modified while they are still wet. Shapes can be sponged out of a wash, clean water can be dripped in to them or additional colours can be dropped in.

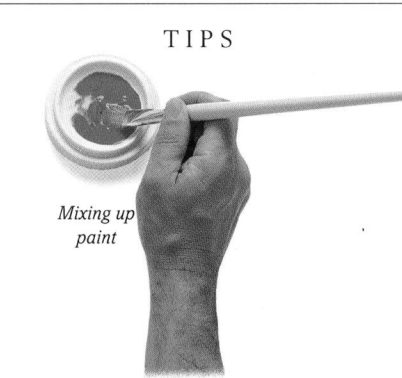

Smooth paper
The colours in the two studies are the same but appear deeper and more vibrant on the smooth paper. Washes should be applied in a continuous, even movement when using smooth paper.

Rough paper
On Rough paper your brushstroke needs to be slower and firmer to ensure that the paint runs into the hollows. In this example the Rough surface has created a "sparkle" effect.

Washing off
Sometimes a wash is not successful or the painting has become too dense with pigment to successfully overlay another colour. If this happens you can wash the whole thing off. You should use cold water to avoid removing the surface sizing on the paper. Very often a washed off painting can look far better than it did before and it requires only minor adjustments to be complete.

The essential feature of a washed off painting is that the texture of the paper is revealed more clearly since the process takes off the top surface – that is the raised parts of a Rough or NOT surface – while the pigment is still lodged in the deeper crevices of the paper. Washing off only ever removes part of a colour. Watercolour is very tenacious once it is lodged in the fibres of the paper. Some pigments have more staining power than others, but most resist the effect of washing off to some degree.

TIPS

Mixing up paint

● Use a bristle brush to mix up the paint but use a soft-hair wash brush, either flat or round, to lay the wash. Make sure you mix up enough paint before you start as you cannot pause to mix up more while you are in the midst of laying the wash.

● Smooth paper will show up any streaks which have been created by (a) not having stirred the paint up well enough, (b) taking too long to apply it, or (c) pushing down too hard with the brush.

● Rough paper will have a sparkle effect in which spots of white paper show through the wash. If you wish to avoid this you may need to work back and forth over the same area several times to ensure that the paint gets into the dips in the surface.

Washing off and overlaying a second wash

Pink wash

1 ▲ Using a Rough paper, paint a blue wash over a section of it.

2 ▲ Wash the blue off under cold water, using a bristle brush to help to dislodge the paint.

3 ▲ Paint a layer of pink over the washed-off blue. You will create a grainy purple.

Wash techniques

Although we tend to think of washes as applications of paint which cover large areas of a painting, the technique is equally suitable for smaller areas. For these you simply use smaller versions of the same brushes, in particular the small round sables. The following swatches are just a few examples of what you can do with washes of colour. Some use the tip of the brush, others the toe and still others involve two brushes being used simultaneously. The possibilities are endless.

A thick application *of Permanent Rose is dragged rapidly across a wet wash of Winsor Blue on a flat 1 inch brush.*

The toe *of a small, round, nylon brush with Permanent Rose is curled swiftly into the Winsor Blue wash to create this suffused vapour trail effect.*

Two drops *of Permanent Rose are dripped into the watery Winsor Blue wash and allowed to spread outwards.*

Using a medium *size, round, soft-hair brush, Permanent Rose is worked rapidly around the edge of this Winsor Blue wash.*

A band of *Manganese Blue and one of Winsor Green are allowed to fuse together. The granulated Manganese Blue wash contrasts with the more even green one.*

Curling a *dark tone of Winsor Green into the granulated Manganese Blue wash gives a quite different effect to that of the colours above.*

Working simultaneously *with two size 8 round brushes, fully charged with dense pigment, can give these rich effects.*

After the *Manganese Blue wash has been applied, the Winsor Green is scrubbed into the paper with a bristle brush.*

Two colours *have been applied on to a flat 1¼ inch wash brush before being dragged quickly across the paper.*

Separate blocks *of Violet and Rose have been applied and allowed to dry before being joined by using a clean, damp brush.*

One thin stroke *of Violet is followed rapidly by another thin stroke of Winsor Green, to create this layered effect.*

The areas *of Winsor Green and of Violet are allowed to run together to create this densely textured, yet fluffy effect.*

APPLYING A WASH WITH A SPONGE

There are a number of ways of applying washes, from the traditional wash brush for standard techniques, to small round brushes for more confined areas, to household wallpaper brushes for very large areas. Some artists, however, like to work with sponges because it allows them to cover large areas more rapidly and effectively. Try laying a wash with several types of sponges to see which you prefer.

1 *To sponge a wash on, mix up a large amount of colour and soak your sponge in it. A small natural sponge is best but you can use a household sponge for larger areas.*

2 *Holding the sponge in your fingertips, rub it back and forth, catching the drips as you go. The technique is to work downwards as if you were cleaning a window.*

GALLERY OF WASHES

SUCCESSFUL WATERCOLOUR PAINTINGS depend to a large extent on the application of washes. Learning to lay washes is a skill that has to be acquired through practice, as it involves an understanding of the amount of paint required to be held in the brush, the degree of dilution of the paint, the nature and angle of the surface being painted and the appropriate choice and handling of the brush itself. Washes can be free-flowing over a large area, with colour blending into colour and with variations of tone, or they can be tightly controlled in small or irregular shaped areas. In addition they can be manipulated wet, so that particular areas can be lifted and lightened, or be altered by having additional colours dropped in.

Gisela Van Oepen, *Pays de l'Aude*
This painting demonstrates clearly the effect of working into very wet areas with dense colour. This can be done either by laying a clear wash over chosen areas and then dropping in the deep colours or by applying colour first and dropping in water or further colours afterwards.

Miles E. Cotman, *A Calm, c.1840-49*
This peaceful scene demonstrates great control in the application of washes. Notice how the uniformity of tone in the wash for the sky is sustained right up to the edges of the clouds. Here there are no dramatic sweeps of the brush, just the kind of consummate skill that allows the image to speak for itself.

Two washes of colour, carefully controlled, are all Cotman needs to realise this sailing vessel in the distance.

Jane Gifford,
Street Scene,
Madras
In this simple yet
effective study, the
artist has carefully
applied her washes in
a form of "patchwork"
to indicate the broad
masses of colour on
the scene. She has
allowed the washes
to move around
freely in areas where
it is appropriate to
the subject to do so,
as on the dome.

The deep blue
wash of the
entrance draws
the viewer into
the centre of
the painting and
forms a striking
counterpoint to
the surrounding
areas.

A couple of
broad, loose
brushstrokes is
all that is needed
to suggest this
woman in her
radiant sari
framed by the
darkness of
the doorway.

Julian Gregg, *Poppit Sands, Cardigan*
In this loosely worked sketch there is practically no overpainting and areas
of the paper are left untouched. The artist has applied simple washes along
the horizontal axis, allowing colours to bleed into each other wet-in-wet
while relying on single, sweeping brushstrokes along the horizon.

Robert Tilling, *Low Tide Light*
Using broad wash brushes, Tilling lays large areas of very
wet colour across his paper, skilfully controlling the paint.
Here the washes are swept across the painting, softening
in tone in particular areas to create the effect of the light.
Certain colours are allowed to bleed into the next to
create an evocative sense of space and mood.

TONE AND COLOUR

AFTER LEARNING TO LAY WASHES, the next stage is to practise building up tone and colour. The easiest way to approach this is to work initially in tones of one colour. In the past it was quite common for artists to paint monochromatic studies, using colours such as Sepia (a dark reddish brown), made from the ink sac of the cuttlefish, and red and brown earth pigments. Other good colours to practise with are blue and black.

Tonal values

Tone is the relative darkness or lightness of an image. If you look at the crumpled paper you will see that although it is white, the play of light over its surface creates a range of tonal contrasts from white to grey. It is these which give the paper its form.

1 ▲ After making a pencil sketch of the plant, apply the palest washes first, in this case a very dilute Indigo, and start filling in the leaves. Notice where the highlights are and leave these areas white.

2 ▲ Look hard at the plant, trying to see the tones rather than the colours. A useful device is to half close your eyes. Once you have distinguished the areas of light and dark, start building up the layers, remembering to let each layer dry before applying the next.

3 ◄ Start working in some of the details, remembering that the areas which are in shadow will be the darkest.

4 ▲ You may find you need a finer brush for the central area, with its intricate array of leaves and flowers.

The delicate flowers of the African Violet are among the lightest areas of tone in this composition. See how the fine outline of the petals serves to throw them into relief.

5 ▲ When you apply very wet washes of paint, you should keep some blotting paper handy in case the colour starts to run.

The sense of the roundness and solidity of the earthenware pot is created by the gradual darkening of tone from left to right, from the area where the light strikes it to the area of shadow.

6 ◀ As you work, you will notice that the colour becomes considerably lighter as it dries. If you need a darker tone of blue, mix in some Payne's Gray with your Indigo. Use the darker mix for the veins in the leaves and for the areas which are in shadow.

If you look closely at this leaf you can almost count the layers of paint that have been applied. It is the contrast between these very dark areas and the lighter ones that give the plant study its three-dimensionality.

Materials

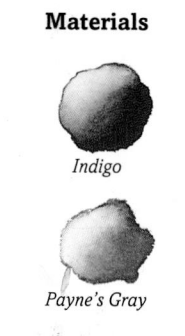

Indigo

Payne's Gray

Size 8 round

OVERLAYING A WASH

Although monochromatic painting is a rewarding technique in its own right, and one with a rich and celebrated history, watercolour painting is more traditionally associated with overlaid washes of colour. To get a clearer idea of the nature of watercolour and the way in which each overlaid colour affects the one below, do a simple painting in tones of one colour and see what happens when you lay a wash of a different colour over it. In the example below the yellow landscape is transformed by the application of a Cerulean Blue wash. Note how the blue over the different shades of yellow results in a broad range of greens even though no green was applied.

Swatches with overlaid blue

Range of yellows, Burnt Sienna and Raw Umber

Effects of Cerulean Blue applied over yellows

BUILDING UP LAYERS

TRADITIONALLY, WATERCOLOUR PAINTING is built up in stages. Since the watercolour medium is generally characterized by transparent colour effects, with the colour of the paper underlying all the painting, the overlaying of colour is, in effect, a form of glazing in which any number of colours may be glazed over each other and each will affect the look of the whole. The most important feature of the technique is that each colour must be completely dry before you paint over it.

Testing colours
It is good practice to try your colours out, both singly and by overlaying them, before committing them to your actual painting. These are the colours used for the painting of the lighthouse.

2 ▲ Once the blue has dried, mix up a wash of Alizarin Crimson and fill in some of the sky area and more of the cliffs. See how the blue shows under the pink and how it is affected by this single layer of overpainting, taking on a purplish hue.

1 ▲ In this exercise you will see how you can create a painting by building up washes of colour. First, with a size 12 wash brush, fill in the sky, sea and cliff areas with a mixture of Cobalt Blue and Payne's Gray.

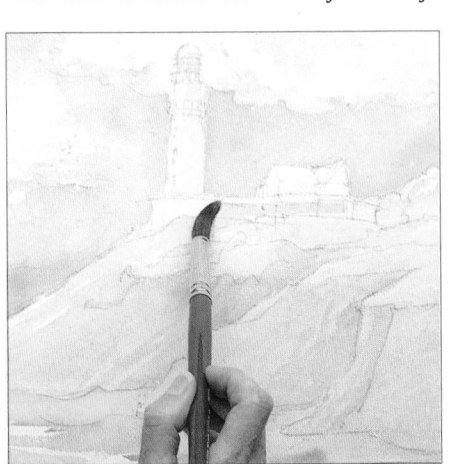

3 ▲ To warm up the colour of the cliffs, add a wash of Raw Sienna. Use this colour also for the basis of the lighthouse, the trees and the grassy areas.

4 ◄ Again, allowing the Raw Sienna to dry, add a layer of Prussian Blue over the trees and grass, building up those areas that need to be darker. Note how the blue over the yellow results in a green, the colour depending on the relative strengths of each.

COMPLEMENTARY COLOURS

The balance of complementary colours plays an important part in painting techniques. If, for example, you are painting a predominantly green landscape, you can create a subtle balance in the colour by laying a bright green wash, letting it dry, and overpainting it with a red one.

In the scene shown below, the sky as well as the foreground area have been overlaid with a red wash, with the poppies forming the final detail. The overall effect is to warm up the landscape, heighten the sense of perspective, and greatly enrich the feel of the work.

Landscape in blues and greens

Landscape with overlaid red wash

5 ◀ To strengthen the tone of the sea, add a second layer of Prussian Blue mixed with Indigo over some of the foreground waves. You will see that the colours appear brighter while the paint is wet, so you may often find that you need to deepen certain colours once your painting has dried.

Lighthouse study
Final touches of blue have been added to give definition to the windows and bring foreground areas into sharper focus.

Note how areas have been left so that the white of the paper forms the clouds and sides of the buildings.

Materials

Cobalt Blue

Payne's Gray

Alizarin Crimson

Raw Sienna

Prussian Blue

Indigo

Size 8 sable / synthetic

Size 12 synthetic

SPONGING OUT

FOR CERTAIN EFFECTS you may need to modify your painting while it is wet, or even after it has dried. For example you might want to create shapes that are lighter in tone in a certain area, in which case it is often easier to apply a broad wash of colour over a complete section of a painting rather than trying to avoid or paint around certain areas.

You can subsequently sponge out or blot out those areas that need to be lighter, a technique known as lifting off. You can do this when the paint is wet or after it has dried, depending on which method is more convenient. The effect is largely the same although lightening areas after the paint has dried may require some vigorous brushwork to dislodge the pigment.

1 ◀ To sponge out cloud shapes, apply a wash of Cerulean Blue plus Mauve with a medium size brush. While the paint is still wet, dip a small natural sponge in water, press it on to the blue wash and remove it in one movement. The sponge will lift off the blue wash.

2 ▶ To practise sponging out from dry paint later, lay a green wash for the bank of the river, making some of the hills in the distance a little darker. Once this has dried, fill in the tree and grass details with a rigger – a fine, pointed brush with long hairs.

3 ◀ Wet your sponge and press it on an area of the sky, holding it there for a moment to loosen the paint. Lift the sponge off and press a sheet of paper towel on to the area that has been wetted. Remove the paper towel to lift the paint off. The sponge will have created cloud-like forms.

4 ▲ To accentuate the shape of the clouds and build up the sky, mix up some Burnt Sienna and Cerulean Blue. With a medium size brush, apply your blue wash to the sky, painting around the whited out cloud areas in order to create shadows and give them a sense of three-dimensionality.

EXAMPLES OF LIFTING OFF

Lifting with brush from dry paint
Here the clouds have been created by working into the sky with a wet bristle brush until the paint has loosened sufficiently to be removed. To dislodge dry paint you will need to use your brush quite vigorously. Some pigment may remain in the paper.

Lifting with paper towel from dry paint
A wet sponge has loosened the dried paint of the sky after which the clouds have been lifted with a paper towel.

Sponging out from wet paint
Here the clouds have been sponged out using a moistened sponge on wet paint. The sponge has been rubbed on to the blue wash and lifted off, taking some of the paint with it. Notice the soft, diffused effect the sponge creates, particularly in comparison to the other methods of lifting off.

5 ▷ In order to lighten the foreground grass, load your brush with clean water and draw it across the area of dry colour you wish to modify. While the water seeps in, work your brush between the trees to create greater definition between them. The degree to which you can wash areas out of your painting will depend on the staining power of the pigments you have used.

6 ◁ Press a sheet of blotting paper on to the wet grass and then remove it. A good deal of the paint will come off. Repeat the process between the trees, first wetting the area you wish to modify with a brush dipped in clean water and then blotting it off with the blotting paper. You may be able to lift a tree out completely in this way.

Riverside study
In this finished version you can clearly see those areas that have been lightened – the clouds, the foreground grass and the details between the trees. What you cannot tell is which areas have been modified while wet and which while dry. It does not make much difference which way you choose to work. It is largely a matter of personal preference and convenience. If you are doing a quick study outdoors you might prefer to sponge out shapes when you get back to your studio.

Materials

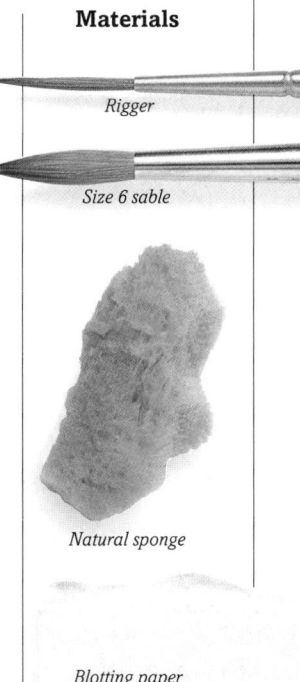

Rigger

Size 6 sable

Natural sponge

Blotting paper

SCRATCHING OUT

Cornish graveyard

IN WATERCOLOUR painting, the technique of scratching out is a means of getting back to the white of the paper or to the dried paint film underneath the one that has just been applied. It can be used for highlights or for particular effects and is as applicable to wet paint films as it is to dry. With wet paint the technique is to scrape the surface with the blunt blade of a penknife taking care not to cut the paper. With dry paint the method is to physically skin the dry paint off the area you want to reveal. The way you handle your blade – making gentle strokes or vigorous ones – will determine the look of the technique.

1 ◀ Using Rough paper, apply a wash of Raw Umber with a one inch brush, starting at the horizon. Dilute the paint as you work your way down; a somewhat patchy effect is fine. Once this has dried, draw a faint pencil outline of the gravestones. Next, take a small round brush and paint a wash of Cerulean Blue over all of the paper, taking care to avoid the gravestones. Apply the blue in loose horizontal strokes. You may have to go over certain areas since paint dries lighter than it appears when it is wet.

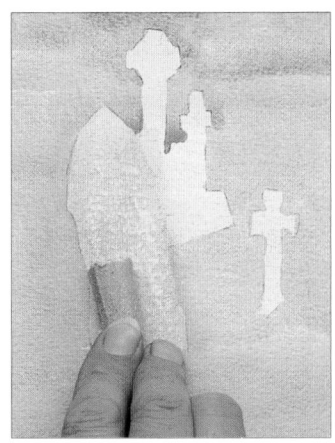

2 ▲ Once the paint has dried, cut a piece of medium grade sandpaper and wrap it around your pencil. Then, using the sandpapered surface, gently scratch the three front stones.

3 ▲ Build up the grass area by adding layers of Aureolin – a bright yellow – and more Cerulean Blue, always allowing the paint to dry between layers. You may use a hair-drier on cool to speed up the process.

Next, take a craft blade and use it to scratch highlights in the sea, pulling the blade down in short vertical strokes (or horizontal ones for headland waves). Notice how the blade reveals the Rough surface of the paper.

4 ▲ Mix Cerulean Blue and Sepia and use your fine, pointed brush to build up the background details. Now take a wet sponge and rub it over an area of dried paint to sponge out a further gravestone.

Materials

Size 8 round brush

1 inch flat brush

6 ◀ Do the same on the second house. The act of skinning these surface layers raises the nap of the paper. You need to burnish (rub down) the paper that you have revealed with your nail or the flat of a paper cutter. This is particularly important if you want to overpaint the area later.

5 ▲ Take a scalpel and gently score around the side of the house, cutting just deep enough to remove the surface of the paper without cutting right through it. Using the blade or a pair of tweezers, lift off the sliver of paper.

7 ◀ To lighten the blue of the horizon and create a feeling of distance in your painting, dip a flat wash brush in clean water and draw it over the area that you want to modify. Allow the water to seep in for a moment.

Medium sandpaper

Craft blade

Scalpel

8 ◀ While the surface is still wet, press a paper towel over the area and then lift the towel off. You will see that the towel removes some of the loosened paint. If you want to make the horizon even lighter, roll a small piece of soft bread over it while the paint is damp. You will find that this picks up still more of the pigment.

Natural sponge

Finished work
For the final touches, the artist has used the wooden end of the brush to "cut" blades of grass in the foreground area while the paint is still wet. She has also rubbed sandpaper over the dried paint film of the gravestones to give them their characteristic coarseness.

Sanding down
certain areas of the grass reveals the roughness of the paper surface.

Paper towel

RESIST TECHNIQUES

Pencil sketch

IF YOU WISH to protect certain areas of your painting so that you can paint over them without disturbing what lies beneath, you can use a method known as masking or stopping out – a "resist" technique. This involves applying masking fluid.

Once the fluid has dried and you have painted over it as much as you wish, you can rub off the masking fluid to expose the protected area of the painting. Masking can be used for highlights, as a means of keeping the paper white, or for safeguarding an area which is light in tone while you deepen the tones around it.

USING MASKING FLUID

1 *Do a pencil drawing of your fox and carefully mask around the edge. Here it has been done in two stages, first with masking fluid applied with a dip pen and then more loosely with a brush.*

2 *Let the masking fluid dry and then dampen the area inside it so that the colours will merge when you apply them. Lay down washes of Burnt Sienna, Cadmium Scarlet and Payne's Gray.*

3 *Once the paint has dried, gently rub off the masking fluid. You can do this in a number of ways, either with a cow gum rubber, a putty rubber, or simply by using your fingers. You will find that the pencil lines are erased in the process.*

1 ▲ Again, starting with a pencil outline, mask out the areas you wish to protect. You can either use an old brush for this as the masking fluid tends to ruin the hairs or protect your brush by rubbing the hairs over a bar of soap before you start. Always wash the brush in warm soapy water as soon as you've finished.

2 ▲ Let the masking fluid dry naturally or speed the process up with a hair-drier. Then, using a medium-size brush, apply a wash of Cobalt Blue and Burnt Sienna over the unmasked areas.

CARE OF YOUR BRUSH

Use an old brush for applying masking fluid and always wash it out in warm soapy water between applications. If you use a good brush, rub the hairs with wet soap before you start. This offers some protection as it prevents the masking fluid from clogging up the ferrule and adhering to the hairs. The lower brush was treated in this way while the top one shows the effects of masking fluid having dried and coagulated on the hairs.

4 ▲ Dry the masking fluid with a hair-drier. You can test it to make sure it is dry by touching it lightly with your fingertips. Next, deepen the tones of the river with a further Burnt Sienna and Cobalt Blue wash.

3 ▲ Apply further washes of Burnt Sienna and Payne's Gray to darken the tones of the trees and the fence, allowing each layer to dry between applications. Then mask out areas of reflection in the river using an old, smallish brush. Wash the brush in warm soapy water as soon as you have finished to stop the masking fluid from ruining the hairs.

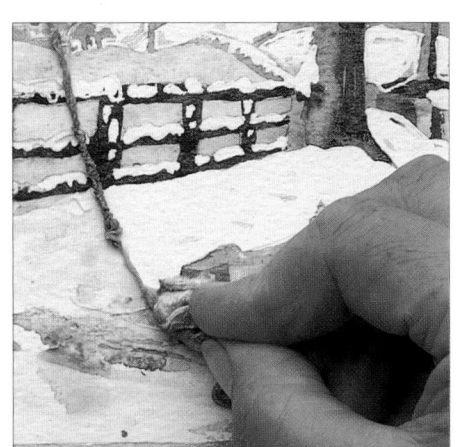

5 ◄ Lift off the masking fluid with a cow gum rubber or a putty rubber. Once it has been removed, fill in the sky with a wash of Alizarin Crimson, Cobalt Blue and Burnt Sienna.

Masking fluid gives a hard edge to any shape that is masked out, a characteristic that can be seen most clearly in the snow-covered fence.

The sky is the final detail to be painted, having been masked from the outset.

Materials

Dip pen

Old size 2 brush, trimmed

Size 1 brush

Size 2 brush

Size 4 brush

Size 6 brush

Winter scene
With the removal of the masking fluid, several things happen: the whiteness of the paper is revealed and the original pencil lines are rubbed out at the same time.

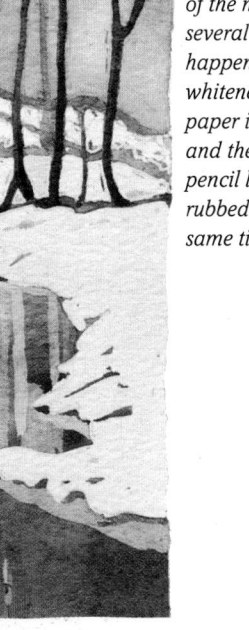

Masking fluid

OTHER RESIST TECHNIQUES

FOR MORE SUBTLE STOPPING OUT effects than those achieved with masking fluid you can use gouache paint, wax or gum arabic. The results are slightly different in each case and the gouache and the gum arabic have to be washed off the paper in order to achieve the resist effect. This means that you are disturbing the colour you have just painted on, so

remember to paint in a deeper tone than the one you want to end up with when you come to paint over the stopped-out areas. The effect of washing off gives a slightly softer-edged feel to the stopped-out area than you would achieve with masking fluid. If you opt for gouache, it is best to use white as this has the least effect on the colours when it is washed off.

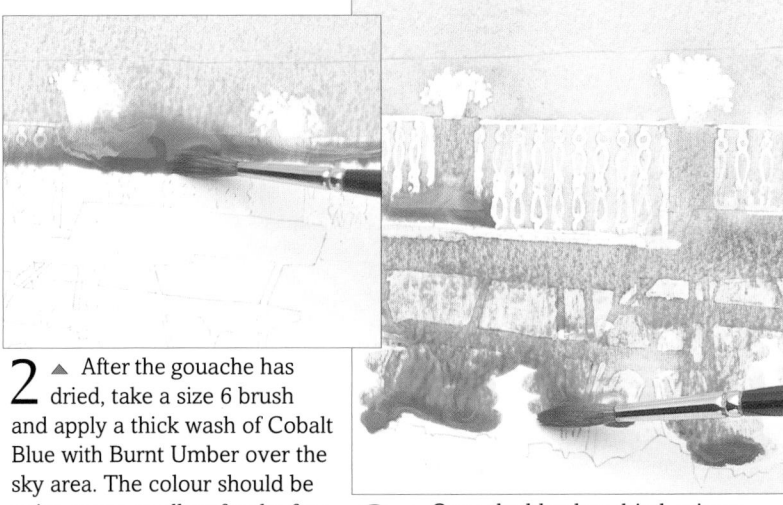

2 ▲ After the gouache has dried, take a size 6 brush and apply a thick wash of Cobalt Blue with Burnt Umber over the sky area. The colour should be quite strong to allow for the fact that some of it will be washed off. See how the gouache paint repels the blue and umber wash.

3 ▲ Once the blue has dried, mix up a wash of Burnt Umber. Apply this smoothly and rapidly to the columns and benches so as not to disturb the gouache.

1 ▲ For gouache resist, draw an outline of the balcony details on a Rough paper and plan which areas will need to be stopped out. Mix up some white gouache paint relatively thickly, like double cream. Then take a very fine brush and paint in the railings and the flowerpots, and a larger brush to paint the balcony floor.

4 ◀ For wax resist, use a sliver of a candle and draw in some foreground grass. Draw additional grass with olive green and light green wax/oil crayons. Both the candle and the crayons will repel washes of colour.

5 ▲ Mix up a wash of Burnt Umber and Viridian and paint it thickly over the foreground area. See how the wash refuses to adhere to the wax-resisted surface. Although the effects are quite subtle, if you look closely you will be able to distinguish individual blades of white and green grass once the wash has dried.

Materials

6 ▶ Add another layer of your blue and umber mix to deepen the colour of the hills. Allow this to dry. Then lower your painting into water and gently sponge over the whole surface. The process will remove the gouache as well as dislodging some of the paint but the candle wax and wax crayon will not be affected. Now stretch your paper on a board and leave it to dry.

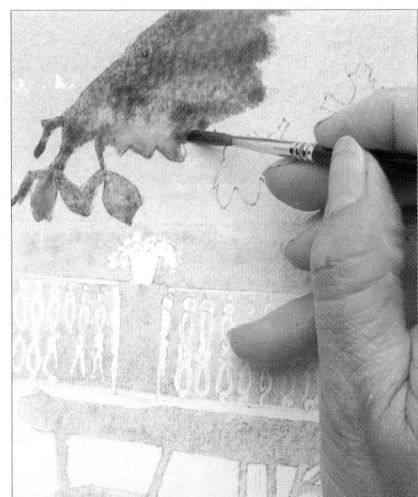

7 ▲ For gum arabic resist, make sure your painting is completely dry and then draw the outline of the overhanging leaves in pencil. Next mix up a wash of Viridian and Cadmium Yellow with equal amounts of gum arabic and water and apply it to the leaves. You can block in large areas of colour since details of sky around the leaves can be lifted out later.

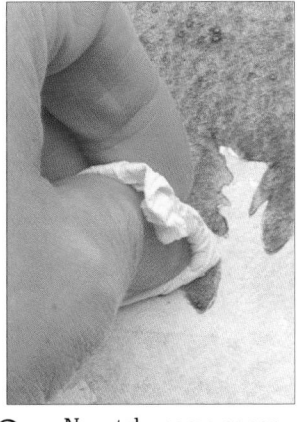

8 ▲ Allow the paint to dry. It will appear quite shiny because of the gum arabic solution. Now dip a fine brush, perhaps a size 1, in water and "paint" an area in the foliage which you wish to lift off later in order to reveal some sky. Allow the water to sink in to the paint for a while.

9 ▲ Now take some paper towel, press it on to the moistened area and lift off the green paint. Because of the gum arabic, it will come off quite easily, without disturbing the blue beneath it.

Final touches

Because the washing off process lifts off some of the paint, details have to be painted in or accentuated later. Here the flowers are painted in Cadmium Scarlet. The columns and the benches are darkened and the shadows are then added as a final stage.

Size 6 brush

Size 1 brush

Wax/oil crayons

Wax candle

Natural sponge

Gum arabic

The white gouache leaves no trace on the paper and yet effectively stops out any colour. It also creates a much softer edge than stopping out with masking fluid.

The wax resist adds texture to the foreground grass.

USING GOUACHE

GOUACHE, OR BODY COLOUR as it is also known, is a watercolour but is one which is characterized by its opacity rather than by the transparent effects normally associated with the medium. Because of its different properties it has specific uses in watercolour painting, for example to create highlights in a traditional watercolour painting or to provide a matt and uniformly even tone when that is what is required. It is generally applied more thickly than a regular watercolour and can create a more impasto effect. Because of its opacity, gouache works particularly well, and economically, on toned or coloured paper.

SINCE GOUACHE PAINT is used more thickly than traditional watercolour, the paint film needs to be a little more flexible. It also needs to flow well to ensure that it can be brushed smoothly out in flat opaque tones. Although gouache colours are made in almost exactly the same way as other watercolours, there are certain modifications which make them marginally more soluble than watercolours, an effect which is noticeable when overpainting them.

Highlights
Gouache paints are traditionally used for highlights, in particular for picking out details on buildings. Their opacity allows them to work well in conjunction with traditional watercolours. In the image on the left, the white gouache creates the sense of form on what might otherwise seem a rather flat, two-dimensional structure.

OVERLAYING GOUACHE

Gouache is basically just another form of watercolour. The paints can be used in the same way as straight watercolour paints, provided they are sufficiently diluted. They can, however, also be used much more thickly, when, for example, a flat uniform tone is required in a particular area, or a more textured look is desired. Between these uses lies a wide range of possible manipulations and effects.

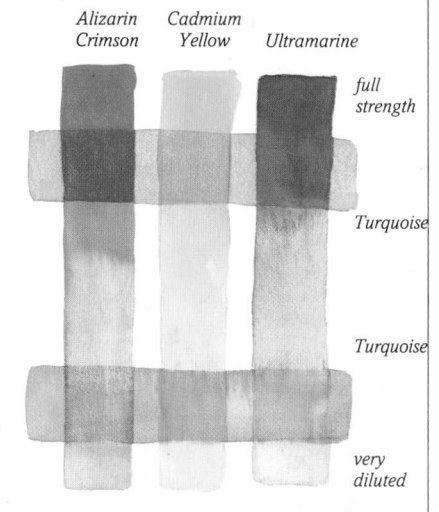

Alizarin Crimson · Cadmium Yellow · Ultramarine

full strength

Turquoise

Turquoise

very diluted

Toned paper
Gouache is particularly effective on lightly toned paper where the background colour serves to unify the whole. To work in this way, begin by sketching in the main features. Then look for the lightest tones and paint them in by adding a touch of colour to the white gouache. Subsequently look for the dark tones and paint them using a more watery mix as above. Although similar to using oils as a technique, the finished appearance is quite different and displays a characteristic chalky mattness.

High pigment loading

The opacity of gouache is often obtained by incorporating very high levels of pigmentation – far more than in watercolour. Gouache paints work well in washes and so can represent good value for money as an alternative to watercolour.

The opaque nature of gouache means that for certain colours there is no other way to get a high level of brightness than to use brilliant but very fugitive pigments. Such colours may be fine for illustrators whose work is designed for reproduction but there is no point in using them in artwork that you wish to be permanent. It is a therefore advisable to check the durability rating before you purchase a gouache colour.

A versatile medium

Having said that, gouache, with its wide range of manipulations and uses, is somewhat more versatile than traditional watercolour paints while being equally easy to handle. It has been used for such a diverse range of subjects as small-scale Indian and Persian miniatures and large-scale studies for oils. When used on a large scale, gouache paints

Transparent and opaque

Gouache can be used in conjunction with transparent techniques or on its own, as in this nude study. Here the artist has exploited the diverse nature of gouache by using it both thickly, as in the face and neck area, and highly diluted, as in the legs. Generally, however, she has chosen to use it more like a traditional watercolour than as an opaque painting medium.

are generally applied with bristle brushes. These are particularly good for both breaking down the paint and for blending it.

Although gouache can be used on its own, either thickly or thinly as in the two examples on this page, it can equally be used in conjunction with traditional watercolours. Indeed, some contemporary artists have made a point of juxtaposing the transparent and opaque techniques of the two forms of watercolour paint in the same work in order to exploit their different natures and effects.

Impasto effects

Gouache can be used thickly, much like oil paints, with the advantage that it dries far more quickly. Here the artist was fascinated by the colours in the water and wanted a water-based medium to capture the shimmering, elusive quality of the fish. The gouache gives the painting a richness and density of tone not possible with transparent techniques.

GALLERY OF TECHNIQUES

THE RANGE OF TECHNIQUES available to the watercolour painter is limited only by the imagination of the individual artist, so you will no doubt devise methods of your own for controlling and manipulating the way you apply the paint. But there are particular techniques that are associated with the medium that range from the way washes are applied, to sponging and scratching out, washing off, wet-in-wet manipulations and various methods of masking out. Also, artists have tried everything from toothbrushes to windscreen wipers for interesting effects.

Note how pattern features throughout this painting, even down to the repeated elements on the rugs. The colours are both muted and vibrant, with an extraordinary richness due to a technique O'Reilly has devised. He has added certain inks and gums to the paint to heighten the textural effects and to give a sense of three-dimensionality to the kilims.

Philip O'Reilly, *Ali Baba Carpet Shop, Kusadasi*
This painting creates pattern through texture and vivid tonal contrasts. Contrary to conventional practice, O'Reilly likes to build up his paintings from dark to light, so that the view from the window here and the sun-drenched rug were his final touches.

Philip Fraser, *Glade in Wood*
This work relies entirely for its effects on the use of masking fluid. Here you can see the characteristic hard-edged shape that shows where the dried masking fluid has protected the paper from the paint, creating suffused areas of light and colour.

**Eric Ravilious,
The Wilmington Giant, 1939**
Here a real sense of scale is created by showing the wire fence large in the foreground and then disappearing into the distance at which point the massive figure of the chalk giant rises across the Sussex Downs. The work is characterized by the use of wax resist where the watercolour is repelled in those areas shaded by the wax.

The roof was painted later with a mixture of traditional watercolour and gouache. It is the gouache which gives the colour its density.

The window details were masked at an early stage to retain the fine lines and clarity of outline.

**Paul Newland,
*Screen and Light***
This unassuming yet atmospheric study in low-key colour explores the idea of pattern and shape. The technique is to float simple flat colour washes into designated areas of the painting. Other areas are left unpainted so it is the paper itself which creates the strong sense of sunlight.

**Colin Kent,
*Evening Cottage***
Fascinated by textures and techniques, Kent chooses smooth paper so that he can create his own surfaces with the paint and with particular methods of application. In this painting he used a pen for the blades of grass, a wallpaper brush for the sky, and a paint-soaked rag for some other areas. He has even been known to use windscreen wipers if they achieve the desired effect.

GLOSSARY

ABSORBENCY The degree to which the paper absorbs the paint, often due to the degree of surface sizing.

ACID-FREE PAPER Paper with a neutral pH that will not darken excessively with age.

ACRYLIC Synthetic resin used in an emulsion as the binding medium for artists' acrylic colours.

ADJACENT COLOURS Literally, those colours closest to each other on the colour wheel, but also used to describe colours which lie next to each other in a painting. Adjacent complementary colours appear brighter as each reinforces the effect of the other.

ADVANCING COLOUR The perception of a colour, usually a warm (orange/red), as being close to the viewer.

AERIAL PERSPECTIVE This describes the effect of atmospheric conditions on our perception of the tone and colour of distant objects. As objects recede towards the horizon they appear lighter in tone and more blue.

AFTER-IMAGE In painting, the visual effect which results from looking at a strong colour, *i.e.* perceiving the complementary colour of the colour we have just been looking at. If, for example, we look hard at an orange-red area and then look at a bright yellow, we might see the yellow as green because we are carrying a blue after-image of the orange-red. This effect is known as colour irradiation.

ARTISTS' QUALITY WATERCOLOUR PAINTS The best quality paints, with high pigment loading and strong colours.

BLEEDING The tendency of some organic pigments to migrate through a superimposed layer of paint.

BINDER In a paint, this is the substance which holds the pigment particles together and which allows them to attach to the support. In the case of watercolour, the binder is water-soluble gum.

BODY COLOUR Also called gouache, a type of paint or painting technique characterized by its opacity.

BURNISHER Traditionally, a piece of polished stone such as agate has been used to burnish gold leaf and similar materials. In watercolour painting, a burnisher is used to smooth down the fibres of the paper when these have been raised by vigorous handling. Some artists use the back of a fingernail for this purpose.

CANNON A cylindrical container used to measure the hairs for brushes.

CHARCOAL Carbonized wood made by charring willow, vine or other twigs in airtight containers. Charcoal is one of the oldest drawing materials.

CHROMA The intensity or saturation of a colour.

CHROMATIC Drawn or painted in a range of colours.

CLAUDE GLASS *see* Reducing glass

COCKLING The buckling of unstretched paper when wetted.

COLOUR IRRADIATION The after-effect which results from looking at a very strong colour in which you perceive its complementary colour. *See also* After-image

COLOUR TEMPERATURE A measurement of colour in degrees Kelvin. This is of importance to photographers who need to correlate the colour temperature of a light source with the type of film they use.

As artists we are aware that the colour temperature of a room illuminated by electric light is significantly different from (yellower than) that of daylight.

COMPLEMENTARY COLOURS Those colours of maximum contrast opposite each other on the colour wheel. For example, the complementary colour of a primary colour is the mixture of the other two primaries, *i.e.* green is the complementary of red because it is made up of yellow and blue, and purple is the complementary of yellow because it is made up of red and blue.

CONTÉ CRAYON A proprietary drawing stick in varying degrees of hardness and in a range of black, white and red earth colours.

COOL COLOURS Generally, a colour such as blue is considered cool. Distant colours appear more blue due to atmospheric effects and cool colours are therefore said to appear to recede.

DEXTRIN Starch made water-soluble by heating. It is used in watercolours as a cheap laternative binder to gum arabic

DURABILITY RATING *see* Lightfastness

EASEL A frame for holding a painting while the artist works on it. Watercolour painters tend to use sketching easels which are of light construction. A good sketching easel allows the painting to be held securely in any position from vertical to horizontal.

ERASER A tool for removing pencil and other marks. In the past, artists used rolled bits of bread or feathers. More recently, artists have used standard rubber erasers, soft putty rubbers or artgum erasers, although the new plastic erasers are extremely clean and versatile.

EXTENDERS Substances such as chalk or barium sulphate are often used in the manufacture of paint, especially when a

A highly absorbent unsized paper

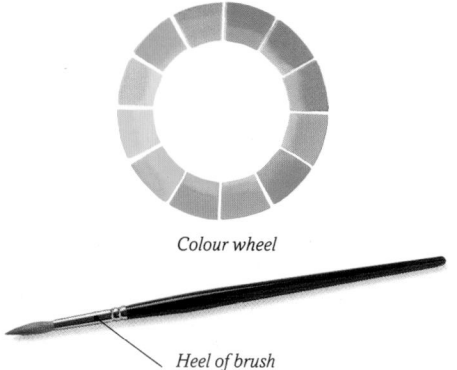

Colour wheel

Heel of brush

The effect of cool colours receding

particular pigment on its own is so strong that it may cause streakiness.

FELTING In paper manufacture, the process by which plant fibres mat together.

FERRULE The metal part of a brush which surrounds and retains the hairs.

FINDER A rectangular hole to the scale of the artist's paper cut in a small piece of cardboard to act as a framing device. This is held up at arm's length and the scene to be drawn or painted is viewed through it.

FIXATIVE A surface coating which prevents charcoal, chalk and conté crayon from becoming dusty and from mixing with overlaid colour.

FLAT WASH An application of an even and uniform area of tone and colour.

FLOCCULATION Like granulation in appearance, but the result of pigment particles coming together as a result of electrical charges rather than the coarseness of the pigment.

FLOTATION The streaky effect made by lighter pigments as they disperse unevenly on the paper.

FOCAL POINT In a painting, the main area of interest visually.

FUGITIVE Colours which are not lightfast and will fade over a period of time.

GLYCERINE The syrupy ingredient of watercolour paints which is used as a humectant or moisture absorber in order to keep them moist.

GOUACHE A type of watercolour paint which is characterized by its opacity.

GOUACHE RESIST Using gouache paint or body colour to protect areas of your paper or paint film from further applications of paint. The gouache is subsequently washed off.

GRADED WASH A wash in which the tones move smoothly from dark to light or from light to dark.

GRANULATION The mottled effect made by heavy coarse pigments as they settle into the hollows of the paper. It may be caused by flocculation *(sic)* or by differences in the specific gravity of the pigments.

GRAPHITE PENCIL Standard pencil leads are made from a mixture of graphite and clay. The mixture is fired and subsequently impregnated with molten wax. The proportion of graphite to clay varies and it is this which determines the hardness or softness of the pencil.

GRAPHITE STICK A large-scale pencil lead used for drawing.

GUM ARABIC Gum from the Acacia tree used as a binding material in the manufacture of watercolour paints. Kordofan gum arabic, which takes its name from the region in Sudan from which it comes, is the main type used nowadays.

GUM ARABIC RESIST Covering details of your painting with gum arabic solution to protect the paper or paint film from further applications of paint. The gum arabic is subsequently washed off. Alternatively, mixing gum arabic with paint allows you to lift the paint off more easily later.

"HARD" WATERCOLOURS Blocks of straight pigment and gum mixes with no added plasticizer or humectant (such as honey or glycerine), which were used by early watercolour artists. The blocks had to be scrubbed to get the colour out but once dry, it could be painted over with little danger of dissolving the paint film.

HEEL OF BRUSH The base of the hairs, near the ferrule.

HIGH-KEY COLOUR Brilliant and saturated colour.

HIGHLIGHT The lightest tone in drawing or painting. In transparent watercolour techniques on white paper, highlights are represented by the white of the paper. In opaque techniques, highlights are represented with opaque white gouache or body colour.

HP OR HOT-PRESSED Paper with a very smooth surface.

Hue Description of a colour such as red etc.

HUMECTANT Moisture-absorbing additive such as glycerine which is used in the manufacture of watercolours to keep them moist.

IMPASTO A thick application of paint.

INTERNAL SIZING Means of reducing the natural absorbency of paper by adding size at the pulp stage. See also Sizing and Surface sizing

LAID PAPER Paper in which you can detect a ladder-like, horizontal and vertical pattern due to the pattern of the wire mould on which it was made.

LATEX *see* Masking fluid

LIFTING OUT The technique which is used to modify colour and create highlights by taking colour off the paper using either a brush or sponge.

LIGHTFASTNESS Permanence (or durability) of a colour measured by the Blue Wool Scale in Britain in which the most permanent colours rate 7 or 8 and ASTM (American Standard Test Measure) in the United States in which the most permanent colours rate 1 or 2.

LOW-KEY COLOUR Muted or unsaturated colour. See also High-key Colour.

Overpainting gouache resisted railing details

Doorway painted in flat washes

A thick, painterly application of gouache paints

MASKING FLUID A solution of latex in ammonia used for masking out particular areas in a painting. It is available in white or pale yellow; when using white paper it is easier to see where the pale yellow has been painted on although there is a very slight risk that the coloured masking fluid will stain the paper.

MASKING OUT The technique of using masking fluid or other materials to protect areas of the watercolour paper while adding washes. With masking fluid, the solution is allowed to dry, paint is applied over it and once that has dried, the masking fluid is gently peeled off.

MONOCHROMATIC Drawn or painted in shades of one colour.

MONOFILAMENTS Individual strands of man-made fibre.

MOULD-MADE PAPER The most common form of high quality watercolour paper is made on a cylinder mould machine. The more random arrangement of the fibres in this process as compared to that on commercial machine-made paper gives far greater strength to the paper.

NICKEL TITANATE A modern inorganic yellow pigment of great permanence.

NOT OR COLD-PRESSED Paper with a fine grain or semi-rough surface.

OPTICAL MIX Colour achieved by the visual effect of overlaying or abutting (placing next to each other) distinct colours rather than by mixing them in a palette.

ORIENTAL PAPER Highly absorbent, hand-made paper which has no internal or surface sizing. Some Japanese papers can weigh as little as 12gsm.

OVERLAYING WASHES The technique of painting one wash over another in order to build up a depth of colour or tone.

OXGALL A wetting agent which helps the paint to flow more easily on the paper.

PERSPECTIVE The method of representing three dimensions on a two-dimensional surface. Linear perspective makes objects appear smaller as they get further away by means of a geometric system of measurement. Aerial perspective creates a sense of depth by using cooler, paler colours in the distance and warmer, brighter colours in the foreground.

PHTHALOCYANINE Modern organic transparent blue and green (chlorinated copper phthalocyanine) pigments of high tinting strengths and excellent lightfastness. Also known by trade names.

PHYSICAL MIX When a colour is arrived at by mixing together several colours on the palette before applying it to the paper.

PIGMENT Solid coloured material in the form of discrete particles which forms the basic component of all types of paint.

PRESERVATIVE Substance added to painting materials to act as a fungicide and bacteriacide. This is particularly important in watercolour as watercolour paints are prone to micro-biological growth.

PRIMARY COLOURS The three colours, red, blue and yellow, which cannot be produced by mixing other colours and which, in different combinations, form the basis of all the other colours.

QUINACRIDONE A modern organic transparent red pigment with very good lightfastness.

RECEDING COLOUR The perception of a colour, usually a cool (blue) one, as being distant from the viewer.

REDUCING GLASS A drawing aid popular in the 18th and 19th centuries. It consisted of a small tinted convex mirror which reflected a reduced and largely monochromatic image of the landscape.

RESIST A method of preventing the paint from coming into contact with the paper or the layer of paint film by interposing a protective coating. Used to preserve highlights, for example, or to retain a particular colour.

ROUGH OR COLD-PRESSED Paper with a rough surface.

SABLE Mink tail hair used to make fine watercolour brushes.

SATURATION The degree of intensity of a colour. Colours can be saturated, *i.e.* vivid and of intense hue, or unsaturated (sometimes known as desaturated), *i.e.* dull, tending towards grey.

SCRATCHING OUT Similar to sgraffito *(sic)*, the process of scratching the surface of the paint (wet or dry) to reveal the paint film or paper which lies below. Can be done with a blade or, in wet paint, with the handle of the brush.

SGRAFFITO A technique, usually involving a scalpel or sharp knife, in which dried paint is scraped off the painted surface. Often used for textural effects.

SECONDARY COLOURS Green, orange and purple, the colours arrived at by mixing two primaries and which lie between them on the colour wheel.

SIZING The coating, either internal or external, of paper. Prepared size usually contains a mixture of gelatine, water and a preservative. The sizing affects the hardness and absorbency of the paper and consequently the way in which the paint will react on it.

SIZING, NEUTRAL A modern size with a neutral pH which replaces the earlier more acidic sizing materials.

SPATTERING A technique which involves flicking paint off the hairs of a bristle brush or a toothbrush with your nail to create an irregular pattern of paint.

Overlaid colour   *The primary colours*

Linear perspective: distant buildings appear smaller

A panoramic vista on Korean paper

Getting back to the paper surface

SPONGING OUT The technique of soaking up paint with a sponge or paper towel so that areas of pigment are lightened or removed from the paper. The technique can be used to rectify mistakes or to create particular effects.

SQUARING UP A grid system used to transfer a sketch or other image accurately to the painting surface. A square grid is superimposed on to the sketch and replicated on the painting surface – often to a larger scale. Complicated areas, as in the girls' faces below, can be given a more detailed grid. The image is then copied square by square from the original image on to the painting surface.

STAINING POWER The degree to which a pigment stains the paper and resists being washed off or scrubbed out. *See also* Tinting Strength.

STENCIL Cut-out image in card or other material through which paint can be sponged or sprayed.

STIPPLING A method of painting involving the application of tiny dots of colour with the tip of the brush.

STRETCHING PAPER The process by which watercolour paper is stretched to prevent it from buckling when paint is applied. The paper is wetted by sponging or dipping briefly in water, it is then attached to a board with gum strip and allowed to dry.

SURFACE The texture of the paper. In Western papers – as opposed to Oriental – the three standard grades of surface are Rough, Hot-pressed (smooth) and NOT or Cold-pressed (semi-rough).

SURFACE SIZING A means of decreasing the absorbency of a painting surface. Commercially available artists' quality watercolour paints are invariably surface-sized in warm gelatine to allow the paper to withstand vigorous treatment.

TERTIARY COLOURS Colours which contain all three primaries.

TINT Colour mixed with white. In the case of watercolour, a similar effect is achieved by thinning the paint with water and allowing more of the white surface of the paper to reflect through it.

TINTING STRENGTH The strength of a particular colour or pigment.

TOE OF BRUSH The tip of the hairs.

TONE The degree of darkness or lightness of a colour. Crumpling a piece of white paper allows you to see a range of tonal contrast.

VARIEGATED WASH A wash in which different colours have been applied in such a way that they run into each other.

VIEWER *see* Finder

WARM COLOUR Generally, a colour such as orange-red is considered warm. In accordance with atmospheric or aerial perspective, warm colours appear to advance towards the viewer whereas cool colours appear to recede.

WASHING OFF The process of dislodging an area of paint, possibly with a bristle brush dipped in water, or a damp sponge.

WATERLEAF A paper with no internal sizing, and which is consequently highly absorbent.

WAX RESIST The process by which wax crayons or a sliver of a candle are used to protect areas of your paper or paint film from further applications of paint.

WEIGHT Watercolour paper is measured in lbs (pounds per ream) or gsm (grammes per square metre). It comes in a large range of weights although the standard machine-made ones are 90lb (190gsm), 140lb (300gsm), 260lb (356gsm) and 300lb (638gsm). The heavier papers, 260lb and over, generally do not need stretching before use.

WET-IN-WET Working with wet paint into wet paint on the surface of the paper.

WOOD-FREE PAPER Good quality paper made from purified, acid-free wood pulp which does not become brittle or yellow with age.

WOVE PAPER Paper in which you can detect the pattern of the wire mould on which it was made, giving it its characteristic woven appearance.

Wet-in-wet technique

A NOTE ON COLOURS, PIGMENTS AND TOXICITY

In recommending Winsor Blue and Winsor Green (which are trade names of the Winsor & Newton Company) we are recommending "phthalocyanine" pigments; other artists' material manufacturers refer to them by their own trade names. These include Phthalo Blue and Green, Monestial Blue and Green and so on. Similarly, in recommending Permanent Rose we are recommending a "quinacridone" pigment. Lemon Yellow Hue, another of our recommended pigments, is also known as Nickel Titanate Yellow. If you have any doubts about which pigment you are buying, refer to the manufacturer's literature.

We have tried to avoid recommending pigments, such as the Chrome colours, which carry a significant health risk. In the case of colours such as the Cadmiums, however, there is nothing commercially available which matches them for colour and permanence. But there is no danger in their use nor in that of other pigments provided artists take sensible precautions and avoid licking brushes with paint on them.

A NOTE ON BRUSHES

The brush sizes given here refer to Winsor & Newton brushes. They may vary slightly from those of other manufacturers.

A NOTE ON PAPERS

The surfaces of papers – Rough, Hot-pressed and NOT (semi-rough), vary noticeably from one manufacturer to another so it is worth looking at several before deciding which to buy.

Photo with overlaid grid

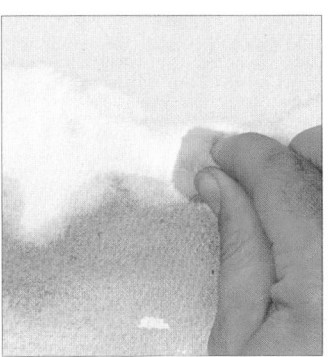

Creating clouds by sponging out paint

INDEX

ACKNOWLEDGEMENTS

Ray Smith would like to thank Alun Foster and Richard Goodban of Winsor & Newton Ltd for their expert advice and Jane Gifford for her lovely fresh paintings. Many thanks also to the team at Dorling Kindersley, including Jane Laing, Sean Moore, Tina Vaughan, Gwen Edmonds and Toni Kay, and in particular to my editor Emma Foa for her patience and skill in managing to get a quart into a pint pot, and to Claire Legemah for her lively and beguiling approach to the design.

Thanks also to Nigel Partridge for his design help in the initial stages of the book, and to Maria D'Orsi for design assistance.